EXERCISE PHYSIOLOGY

AND FUNCTIONAL ANATOMY

EXERCISE PHYSIOLOGY

AND FUNCTIONAL ANATOMY

COLIN CLEGG

FELTHAM PRESS

Copyright © C. A. Clegg 1995

First Published by Feltham Press 1995
Reprinted by Feltham Press 1995
Reprinted by Feltham Press with additions in colour Spring 1996
Reprinted by Feltham Press Autumn 1996

British Library Cataloguing-in-Publication Data.

A catalogue record for this book is available
from the British Library.

EXERCISE PHYSIOLOGY

CONTENTS

ACKNOWLEDGMENTS

Thanks are especially due to Dr Jo Doust of the Chelsea School of Physical Education, Sport Science, Dance and Leisure, University of Brighton, who most generously gave of his valuable time to read the entire manuscript, and who made many constructive suggestions which were of the greatest help to the author.

I would also like to thank Dr David Parry of King's College Hospital and Dr Barry Mitchell of the Anglo-European College of Chiropractic, Bournemouth, for help with the anatomy section. I would also like to thank Steve Mayer, and James Leaver for their help in the final stages of the preparation of the manuscript, and Chris Hanks for his encouraging comments.

I am especially grateful to Sam Denley of Feltham Press who devoted much care and attention to the creation of the artwork and to the design and production of the book as a whole, also to Steve Lucas for his assistance with the preparation of the colour plates in the anatomy section.

Finally, I would like to express my gratitude to my wife Ann, without whose help and support the entire project would not have been possible.

PREFACE

The aim of this book is to provide a concise but comprehensive introduction to the main ways in which the human body responds to the demands of exercise.

Exercise typically involves movement; but there are elements within exercise which may be static, involving tension and balance. Exercise may also be either concentrated into a short period of intense activity, or sustained over a longer time. Whatever the type of exercise, the body systems adjust and adapt to it, both in the short term and the long term – some more dramatically than others. The study of how the body adapts to the demands of exercise is known as **Exercise Physiology**.

Although the huge number of sports and activities available involve a wide variety of actions, they all have certain major interacting systems in common, and it is on these that attention will be focussed in this book.

Exercise always involves muscular activity, so that **Muscles and Bones in Action** is a good starting point for the study of exercise physiology.

The **Energy Relations** of muscular activity are critical, as without a continuous supply of energy, muscular contraction is not possible.

The increased use of energy by muscles during exercise results in an increase in the demand for fuel and oxygen, and in the production of waste products. Therefore the **Circulation**; and **Breathing, Gas Exchange and Transport** systems adapt accordingly.

Other body systems are also involved in the response to exercise, but they either do not show such specific adaptations as those mentioned above, or they may be so closely involved with them, that they are difficult to deal with independently. Therefore these systems are either dealt with as their involvement arises, or in the Chapter on **Exercise, Fitness and Health**, where consideration is also given to the changing response of the body with age.

Training and performance applications are highlighted in sections throughout wherever relevant; and the broader principles of training are dealt with in the Chapter on **Training Principles**.

Key Points of special importance are summarised at the end of each chapter.

Photocopiable packs for staff/student use on **Measurement and Testing of Physical Performance**, and of **Assignments and Solutions** designed to help students work through this book, encourage self-appraisal, and develop examination technique, are available to accompany this volume.

1 MUSCLES AND BONES IN ACTION

OBJECTIVES

To enable the reader to understand the following.

❖ The structure of skeletal muscle.

❖ How the sliding filament mechanism works in muscle contraction.

❖ The different types of muscle fibre, and their use during exercise.

❖ Muscle fibre types as predictors of performance.

❖ The effect of training on muscle fibres.

❖ Motor units.

❖ How muscle fibres are stimulated by nerves.

❖ Muscle fatigue.

❖ The role of proprioceptors in muscle contraction.

❖ Muscles and bones in action.

1.1 STRUCTURE OF A SKELETAL MUSCLE

A skeletal muscle consists of bundles of muscle fibres that have a striped or striated appearance under the microscope.

The muscle fibres can be up to several centimetres long and can branch. They do not usually run from one end of the muscle to the other, and where they overlap they are bound together by connective tissue. The connective tissue sheaths that bind the muscle fibres together are continuous with each other, and ultimately, with the tendons at each end of the muscle, so that contraction of the fibres is transmitted efficiently via the tendons to the bones of the skeleton.

Figure 1.1: *Structure of a skeletal muscle.*

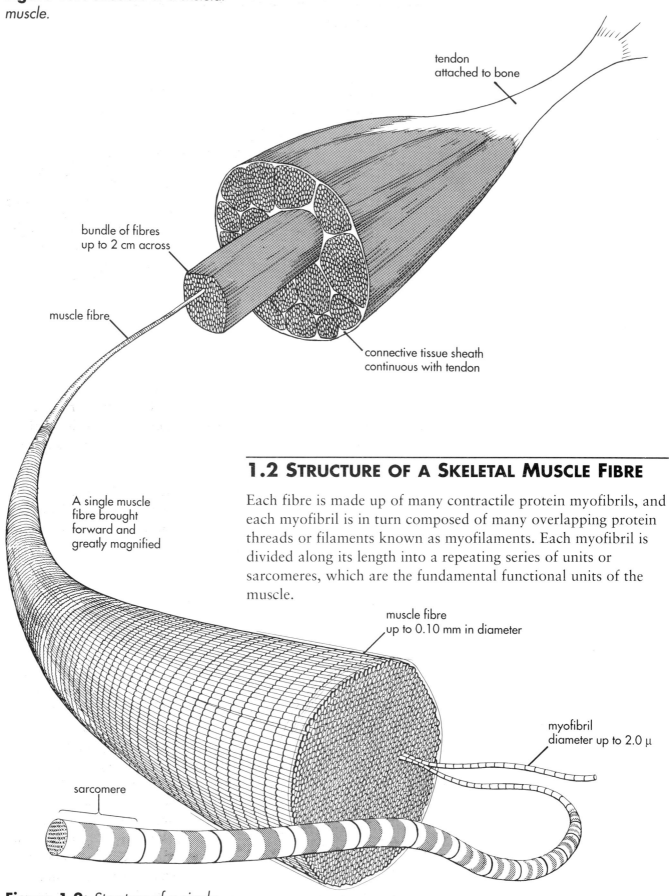

tendon attached to bone

bundle of fibres up to 2 cm across

muscle fibre

connective tissue sheath continuous with tendon

A single muscle fibre brought forward and greatly magnified

1.2 STRUCTURE OF A SKELETAL MUSCLE FIBRE

Each fibre is made up of many contractile protein myofibrils, and each myofibril is in turn composed of many overlapping protein threads or filaments known as myofilaments. Each myofibril is divided along its length into a repeating series of units or sarcomeres, which are the fundamental functional units of the muscle.

muscle fibre up to 0.10 mm in diameter

myofibril diameter up to 2.0 μ

sarcomere

Figure 1.2: *Structure of a single muscle fibre.*

1.3 STRUCTURE AND FUNCTION OF A SARCOMERE

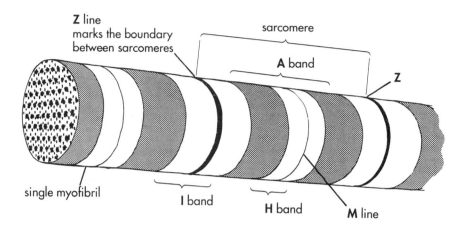

Figure 1.3: *The striated appearance of a sarcomere.*

The protein myofilaments of the sarcomere are of two main types; thin filaments of actin, and thicker filaments of myosin. The overlapping arrangement of these filaments gives rise to the striped or striated appearance of the fibres when observed under the microscope.

The sarcomere contracts as a result of these overlapping filaments sliding over each other, in what is known as the sliding filament mechanism. The simultaneous contraction of each sarcomere results in the contraction of the muscle fibre as a whole.

1.3.1 SLIDING FILAMENT MECHANISM

When stimulated by a motor nerve impulse, the actin filaments which are attached to the Z discs at the end of each sarcomere, are slid between the myosin filaments, drawing the Z discs closer together. This causes each sarcomere to shorten. The sliding action is operated by a series of cross bridges between the filaments. These cross bridges move the actin filaments actively one way, but not the other way on their recovery stroke, thus explaining why the sarcomere, and therefore the muscle as a whole, is only effective in contraction, and cannot actively restretch itself. Typically a contracted muscle is restretched by the contraction of an opposing muscle *(Section 1.10)*. If a muscle is overstretched, then the elasticity of its component tissues restore it to its original length. If an immovable resistance prevents the contraction of the muscle as a whole, the sarcomeres may still contract a certain amount by stretching the elastic component of the muscle instead of moving the bone*(s)* to which they are attached.

Figure 1.4: *Sliding filament mechanism.*

An electronmicrograph of a cross-section of a skeletal muscle fibril *(x 112 000)*

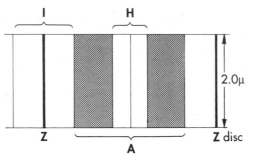

a) Sarcomere of relaxed muscle as seen under the microscope.

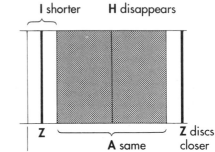

b) Sarcomere of contracted muscle as seen under the microscope.

Hexagonal arrangement of thick *(myosin)* and thin *(actin)* filaments shown in cross section in greater detail.

c) Diagramatic explanation of how the banding pattern is due to differing densities of overlapping actin and myosin filaments.

d) As for **c** but actin filaments have slid to the middle of the sarcomere and met in the centre, pulling the **Z** discs closer together.

Sarcomere lengths		
Fully extended	3.6μ	100%
At rest	2.2μ	59%
Fully contracted	1.6μ	44%

The force generated by a muscle is related to the degree of overlap of the actin and myosin filaments, which in turn determines the number of cross bridges that can be formed at any one time. For example, the more a muscle is stretched past an optimum length, the smaller the force that can be exerted, as there is less and less overlap between the filaments, and fewer and fewer cross bridges that can be formed.

1.3.2 MOLECULAR BASIS OF SLIDING FILAMENT MECHANISM

The myosin filaments have protein projections or cross bridges or 'heads' which extend towards the actin filaments. When the muscle is at rest the myosin cross bridges are not connected to the actin filaments, and an ATP molecule is bound to the free end of each cross bridge.

The actin filaments are associated with two other proteins which are involved in control of the contraction mechanism, namely **tropomyosin** and **troponin**.

In the absence of free calcium ions, tropomyosin and troponin prevent the connection of the cross bridges between the myosin and actin filaments.

The spread of an excitatory impulse throughout the muscle fibres, causes the release of calcium ions from the sarcoplasmic reticulum *(a system of membranous sacs)* around the myofibrils. Troponin has a high affinity for calcium ions, and in their presence the inhibitory effect of tropomyosin and troponin is removed, and the myosin cross bridges connect with the actin.

Figure 1.5: *Diagrammatic model of cross bridge action.*

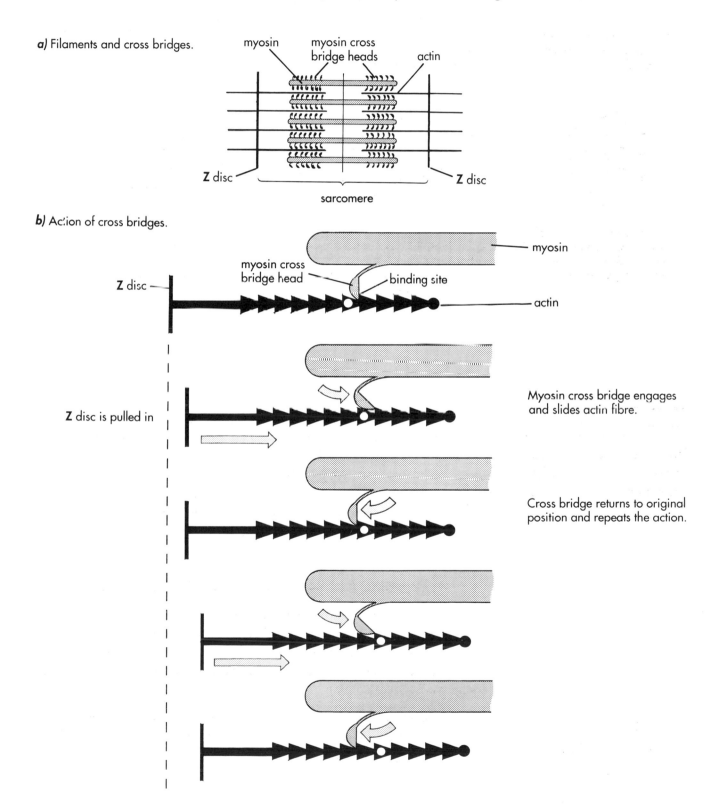

a) Filaments and cross bridges.

b) Action of cross bridges.

1.3.3 ROLE OF ATP

The coupling of actin and myosin forms an **actomyosin** complex. The formation of this complex activates an enzyme, myosin-ATPase, which catalyses the breakdown of ATP with the release of energy.

$$ATP \rightarrow ADP + P + Energy$$

The released energy is used to move the cross bridges actively in one direction, which in a normal contraction *(in which the muscle shortens)* causes the actin filaments to be slid over the myosin filaments towards the centre of the sarcomere, thus pulling the Z discs at each end of the sarcomere closer together so that the muscle contracts.

The cross bridge connection is broken by the combination of another ATP molecule with the actomyosin.

$$Actomyosin + ATP \rightarrow Actin + Myosin/ATP$$

As a result a single cross bridge may undergo many reconnections per second with the actin filament during a muscle contraction.

The cross bridges operate out of phase with each other, so that at any one time about half are attached, whilst the others are recovering, thus providing a smooth steady action.

The coupling and uncoupling of the cross bridges between the myosin and actin filaments continues as long as there are sufficient calcium ions available to inhibit the troponin-tropomyosin system (this will be the case as long as the muscle is being stimulated), and as long as ATP is available - in the absence of ATP the cross bridges remain coupled and the muscle remains in contraction (rigor).

1.3.4 MUSCLE RELAXATION

When the motor nerve impulse stops, the calcium ions are actively pumped back into the sarcoplasmic reticulum, and the troponin-tropomyosin system resumes the blocking of the cross bridge connections. At the same time the myosin-ATPase activity decreases and therefore ATP is not broken down and energy is not released, no tension is generated, and the muscle is relaxed.

1.4 TYPES OF MUSCLE FIBRE

Two main types of striated skeletal muscle can be distinguished on the basis of their speed of contraction, namely **Slow Twitch** *(ST)* and **Fast Twitch** *(FT)* fibres. Human skeletal muscles consist of mixtures of each type of fibre.

The relative proportion of each fibre type varies in the same muscles of different people, and in different muscles within the same person. For example; elite marathon runners can have a greater proportion of ST fibres in their leg muscles, and elite sprinters more FT fibres, but this is not always the case *(Section 1.4.5)*. Within the same person the soleus muscle in the calf has a greater proportion of ST fibres, possibly as it is primarily a postural muscle involved in maintaining balance over long periods of time; and the triceps muscle in the arm has a greater proportion of FT fibres.

1.4.1 SLOW TWITCH MUSCLE FIBRES *(ST)* or TYPE I

These have a slower contraction time than the fast twitch fibres, and they are better adapted to low intensity, long duration endurance work. They have a high capacity for aerobic respiration as a result of several modifications. For example, they have a better blood supply as a result of a greater number of capillaries per fibre than the fast twitch fibres. Slow twitch fibres have more myoglobin, which is a red muscle pigment that combines with oxygen, and for this reason they can also be called 'red fibres'. Myoglobin has a greater affinity for oxygen than haemoglobin, it thus 'robs' oxygen from the oxyhaemoglobin in the blood, and in turn acts as a store of oxygen within the muscle, releasing it to the mitochondria *(microscopic structures in the fibres which are the centres of aerobic respiration.)*. Slow twitch fibres also have more mitochondria, with their associated enzymes for aerobic respiration, than the fast twitch fibres.

These adaptations result in a greater ability to utilise oxygen, known as the **oxidative potential**, so they are also sometimes called Slow Oxidative *(SO)* fibres.

1.4.2 FAST TWITCH MUSCLE FIBRES *(FT)* or TYPE II

These have a faster contraction time, generate a greater force of contraction, and are better adapted to high intensity short duration work. They have a low aerobic capacity; having less capillaries per fibre, less myoglobin *(therefore also being known as 'white fibres')*, and fewer and smaller mitochondria than the ST fibres. As a result, they produce ATP mainly by the lactic acid system of anaerobic glycolysis. For this reason they can also be referred to as Fast Glycolytic *(FG)* fibres.

1.4.3 SUMMARY OF MUSCLE FIBRE TYPES

Although it is convenient to deal with muscle fibres as being either slow twitch or fast twitch, there is in fact a range of fibre types including those that have a mixture of oxidative and glycolytic properties *(Type IIa or FTa or Fast Oxidative-Glycolytic (FOG))*, see Table 1.1.

Table 1.1: *Types of muscle fibres.*

I	Slow Twitch *(ST)*, or Slow Oxidative *(SO)*
IIa	Fast Twitch *(FTa)* or Fast Oxidative–Glycolytic *(FOG)*
IIb	Fast Twitch *(FTb)* or Fast Glycolytic *(FG)*

❖ *Training and Performance Applications*

The proportion of different muscle fibre types in the different muscles, which is largely inherited, explains the high specificity of training, and the specialisation of different individuals to individual sports. However, in addition to the fibres described above, another group of relatively unspecialised fibres can be identified if special staining techniques are used. These are the Type IIc or undifferentiated fibres, which make up less than 5% of the total fibres. It is suggested that endurance training can result in Type IIb being converted into Type IIa, and that these Type IIc could be fibres in transition between the two. This would go some way in explaining why too much long steady work in running can result in a loss of speed.

With age the total number of fibres is reduced, with a reduction of maximum oxygen consumption and strength, which results in a dramatic drop in athletic ability.

1.4.4 USE OF MUSCLE FIBRE TYPES DURING EXERCISE

All the different types of fibre are used *(recruited)* in all types of exercise. For example, although the slow twitch fibres are particularly adapted to low intensity aerobic endurance work, they are always recruited at the start of exercise, independent of the intensity of the exercise. Similarly, although the fast twitch fibres are particularly adapted to high intensity anaerobic activities involving all out rapid powerful movements, they are also progressively recruited during low intensity endurance work as fatigue increases.

However, considering a situation within a muscle where there is a gradual increase in the force of contraction, there is an overall increase in involvement of fibres from Type I *(SO)*, to IIa *(FOG)* to IIb *(FG)*.

❖ *Training and Performance Applications*

In order to train the whole muscle for strength (the maximum force that can be exerted in a single effort), and power (the amount of work that can be achieved in a certain time), it must be subjected to maximum stress, thus engaging as many fibres at the same time as possible. In weight training for example, many repetitions of an easily managed load will improve muscle endurance, but only engage relatively few fibres at any one time. Whereas a few repetitions of near maximum load, will improve muscle strength and power, by engaging virtually all the muscle fibres at once. As with all training, gains are only made as a result of progressive overload, along with adequate recovery periods.

1.4.5 MUSCLE FIBRE TYPES AS PREDICTORS OF PERFORMANCE

Rather surprisingly the proportion of the different types of fibres in the leg muscles is not a good basis for the prediction of performance. For example some elite marathon runners have a greater percentage of fast twitch fibres than some elite sprinters, and some elite sprinters have a greater percentage of slow twitch fibres than some elite marathon runners.

❖ *Training and Performance Applications*

In man it would appear that the number of fibres within a particular muscle is fixed early in life. Any increase in muscle size (cross sectional area) as a result of training is due to an increase in the size of the fibres (hypertrophy) already present, rather than to an increase in the number of fibres by longitudinal division. This increase in size is due to an increase in the number and size of myofibrils per fibre, with an associated increase in the amount of proteins, especially myosin.

The greater the number of fibres (which cannot be increased by training), and the greater the cross sectional area (which can be increased by training) the greater the strength of the muscle, although some increases in strength are due to the central nervous system developing the capacity to recruit more motor units into simultaneous contraction.

Training affects all fibre types in the same way. For example endurance training results in an increase in the capillary density, and in the number and size of mitochondria in all fibre types. In fact one of the most significant adaptations to endurance training is an increase in the activity of the enzymes associated with aerobic respiration in the mitochondria, with up to a doubling of their ability to produce ATP.

The fact that successful performance is possible without the optimum proportion of fibre types, is illustrated by the observation that endurance training can raise the oxidative capacity of fast twitch fibres even above that of slow twitch fibres in an untrained subject. Similarly, power training results in an increase in the glycolytic or anaerobic potential of both slow twitch and fast twitch fibres. However, the cross sectional area of fast twitch fibres increases more than that of the slow twitch fibres with strength training.

Although the aerobic and anaerobic capacities of all fibre types can be improved by training, the contraction times of the respective types remain unaltered.

Table 1.2: *Comparison of percentage fibre compositions of different categories of athlete.*

	Range of % ST fibres	Average % ST fibres
Male marathon runners	50 – 95	85
Male 800m runners	50 – 80	55
Male sprinters	20 – 55	35

Table 1.3: *Summary of differences between fast and slow twitch muscle fibres.*

Characteristic	ST Type I (SO)	FT Type II	
		Type IIa (FOG)	Type IIb (FG)
Contraction time	Slow (110 ms)	Fast (50 ms)	Fast (50 ms)
Aerobic capacity	High	High	Low
Anaerobic capacity	Low	High	High
Force of contraction	Low	High	High
Mitochondrial number	High	High	Low
Myoglobin content	High	Medium	Low
Phosphocreatine store	Low	High	High
Glycogen store	Medium	High	High
Elasticity	Low	High	High
Activity level of myosin ATP-ase	Low	High	High
Amount of sarcoplasmic reticulum and rate of calcium release	Low	High	High
Muscle fibre	Small diameter	Large	Large
Excitability	Low	High	High

1.5 MOTOR UNITS

Skeletal muscles are stimulated by motor nerves. Each motor nerve contains many motor neurones or nerve cells, but there are far more muscle fibres than there are motor neurones, therefore each motor neurone must supply more than one muscle fibre. A motor neurone and the muscle fibres it stimulates, act as a unit, and are together known as a **motor unit**.

The number of muscle fibres stimulated by a single motor neurone can vary from as few as 5, giving very fine control, for example in the muscles that move the eye in its socket; to as many as 2000, for example, in the quadriceps muscle at the front of the thigh, where control is correspondingly less fine.

1.5.1 MOTOR UNIT TYPES

Muscle fibres in a particular motor unit are all of the same type. Indeed the fibre type of a motor unit is mainly *(but not entirely)* determined by the nature of the motor neurone supplying it. This is illustrated by the fact that the only clear case of one type of muscle fibre being converted to another, is when a motor neurone supplying fast Type II muscle fibres is switched surgically to supply slow Type I muscle fibres, and vice versa. Fast fibres are in fact converted to slow fibres more easily than the reverse. Because of this interconvertibility it is perhaps more correct to refer to 'slow' and 'fast' motor units rather than muscle fibres.

Table 1.4: *Comparison of neurone types.*

Motor Neurone	Supplying Muscle Fibre Type	
	I *(ST)*	II *(FT)*
Cross section area of nerve fibre	Smaller	Larger
Conduction Velocity	Slow	Fast

1.6 NERVOUS STIMULATION OF MUSCLE FIBRE

At the point of contact with the muscle fibre, the motor neurone terminates in a motor end plate, otherwise known as the neuromuscular or myoneural junction. This is where the nerve impulse stimulates the muscle fibre.

Figure 1.6: *A neuromuscular junction as seen in section.*

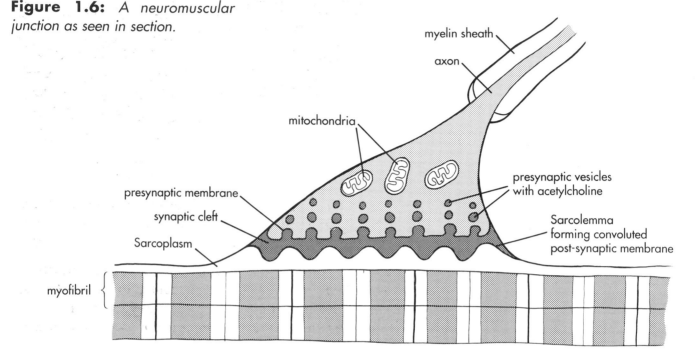

When a nerve impulse arrives at the motor end plate, the presynaptic vesicles release the neurotransmitter substance acetylcholine. This diffuses across the gap *(known as the synaptic cleft)* between the motor end plate and the post-synaptic membrane of the muscle, and initiates a wave of electrical activity *(an excitatory post synaptic action potential (EPSP))* in the post synaptic membrane. If the EPSP exceeds a certain threshold it will initiate a contraction of the muscle fibres in the motor unit. If it does not, but the nerve impulses are repeated at a high enough frequency, the successive discharges from the presynaptic membrane add up or summate, resulting in an increased EPSP which is effective. Generally speaking slow twitch muscle fibres are less excitable than fast twitch muscle fibres.

After the action is completed the enzyme cholinesterase breaks down the acetylcholine, thus clearing the gap in readiness for the arrival of another impulse at the motor end plate.

1.6.1 TRANSMISSION WITHIN THE MUSCLE FIBRE

The action potential spreads rapidly over the surface membrane of the fibre and throughout all the myofibrils via in-turnings of the membrane, known as T tubules. The T tubules are in close association with the sarcoplasmic reticulum around each myofibril.

Figure 1.7: *Sarcoplasmic reticulum.*

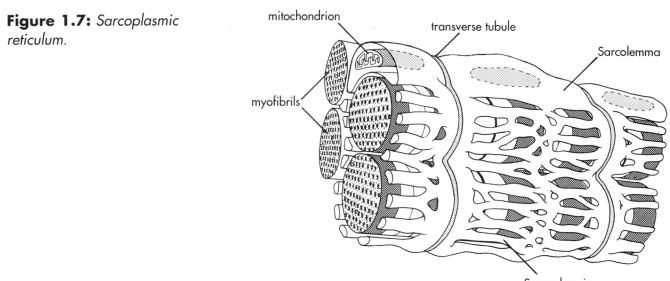

The arrival of the action potential triggers the release of calcium ions from the sarcoplasmic reticulum vesicles. This event initiates the contraction process, as previously described *(Section1.3.2).*

As a result of the arrangement of the T tubules, which penetrate all parts of the fibre, all the myofibrils contract together. Also as each muscle fibre in a motor unit receives the motor nerve impulse at the same time, all the fibres in a motor unit contract together.

1.6.2 RESPONSE OF MUSCLE TO STIMULATION

Nerve impulses are all of the same strength or magnitude, and travel along the motor nerve fibre or axon either at full strength or not at all, obeying what is known as the 'all or nothing law'. Under certain conditions muscle fibres and therefore motor units, also obey this law and either contract completely or not at all. However, the degree of muscle fibre contraction can decrease as the fibres fatigue, or it may even increase as a result of a previous stimulation.

Variation in the strength of the muscle response as a whole is achieved in different ways. One method of varying the strength of the muscle contraction, is achieved by what is known as **spatial summation** or **multiple motor unit summation**, in which the number and the size of the motor units recruited throughout the muscle as a whole are varied. A staggered spread of activation of the motor units throughout the muscle, also enables sustained contractions to be maintained, as some motor units are contracting whilst others are relaxing. In this way the use of ATP, and the associated fatigue, is spread throughout the muscle, instead of being confined to certain units.

Another method of varying the strength of the muscle contraction involves the frequency of motor nerve impulses. If the frequency of motor nerve impulses is such that the next impulse reaches a muscle before it has completely relaxed after the previous contraction, it starts the second contraction from a higher force level, so that the resulting force is greater than that from a single stimulus. This adding together or **wave summation** of contractions can lead, if the impulses arrive so fast that there is no time for any relaxation, to a complete fusion of the contractions, which endures as long as the stimuli persist, or until the muscle fatigues.

❖ *Training and Performance Applications*

A type of complete fusion of contractions experienced by many sportspersons is muscle cramps. These can occur during exercise, usually after strenuous effort in hot conditions, or even whilst inactive. Although correct conditioning in a controlled training programme can reduce the risk of muscle cramps, there is no clear explanation of why these cramps occur. They are generally short lasting and cannot be reliably reproduced under controlled conditions, so it is not possible to investigate all the factors that might be involved in causing them. Suggested explanations include imbalances in the normal amounts of sodium, potassium, and chloride ions on either side of the muscle membranes, and/or a failure to withdraw calcium ions back into the sarcoplasmic reticulum at the end of the stimulation of the muscle for some reason.

1.7 MUSCLE FATIGUE

Although it is obvious that muscles tire as a result of strenuous use, such are the complexities of muscle physiology that the causes of muscle fatigue are not easily identified. Contributing factors include the following.

Interruption of neuromuscular events.
Depletion of the neurotransmitter substance acetylcholine, which is released by the motor neurones at the neuromuscular junction, reduces the stimulation of the muscles. This would appear to be more common with fast twitch motor units, and could help explain why they fatigue more rapidly compared with the slow twitch motor units.

Once the muscle membranes are stimulated, the impulse may not be propagated throughout the muscle due to an imbalance between sodium and potassium ions across the muscle membranes.

Once the impulse reaches the muscle fibres, there may be reduced calcium ion release, resulting in reduced cross bridge formation. This reduced calcium ion release may be due to either temporary T-tubule damage, or the inhibiting effect of accumulating lactic acid.

Depletion of the sources of energy.
Fatigue will result as it becomes increasingly difficult to replenish supplies of ATP *(Chapter 2 Section 2.4, p 43)*. If phosphocreatine stores are depleted, as they are when running the 100 and 200 metres for example, maximum power cannot be maintained.

Depletion of muscle and liver glycogen produces a variety of effects, all of which contribute to fatigue. Glycogen is a readily available source of energy under both aerobic and anaerobic conditions, and as the stores are used up, the same level of activity cannot be maintained. Also, fatty acids from the fat stores cannot be fully oxidised to release all their energy if there is insufficient breakdown of carbohydrates at the same time. Under these conditions poisonous by-products accumulate, leading to the rapid onset of fatigue.

The depletion of a substance called carnitine, which aids the transport of the fatty acids into the mitochondria, where they are oxidised, also contributes to fatigue.

Alterations in the concentration of the body fluids.
Loss of water from the body, and therefore also the muscles, will disturb ion balance and lead to disruption of normal functioning as described before. Water loss can also contribute to an increase in body temperature due to a decrease in sweating as dehydration sets in *(Chapter 2 Section 2.8, p 54)*.

Increase in body temperature.
Active muscle rapidly heats up by about 2-3°C. Generally this is beneficial as it speeds up the rate of enzyme catalysed reactions involved in muscle contraction, and increases the amount of oxygen liberated from the oxyhaemoglobin in the muscle capillaries. However, an increase of more than 2-3°C can disrupt the balanced biochemistry of muscle metabolism, quickly leading to fatigue.

Insufficient blood supply.
An insufficient blood flow to the muscles will increase most of these factors contributing to fatigue, particularly by not delivering sufficient oxygen to maintain aerobic respiration. One cause of this in prolonged exercise in the vertical position is postural hypotension, where blood accumulates in the veins of the lower parts of the legs, reducing cardiac output as a result of reduced return of blood to the heart.

As the oxidation of fat requires more oxygen than the oxidation of glucose, the increasing use of fat during exercise increases the problem of oxygen shortage. With insufficient oxygen, respiration

❖ *Training and Performance Applications*

Stretching plays an important role in training and just before competition. If a muscle is suddenly stretched, as are the hamstrings in a bouncing style of toe touching exercise, the **stretch reflex** *is activated. The muscle spindles detect the stretch and trigger an opposing reflex contraction of the muscle being stretched. Such 'stretching' exercises are therefore counter-productive, as the muscle contracts to protect itself. The strength of the stretch reflex depends on the speed of the stretch. The faster the stretch, the stronger the reflex contraction of the muscle being stretched. Sustained stretching leads to a reduction in the signals from the muscle spindles, and the stretch reflex is decreased in strength in a process known as* **habituation**.

The connective tissue that binds muscle fibres together into bundles, and which is continuous with the tendons that connect the muscles to bone, is capable of being stretched to a certain degree, and the muscle fibres themselves grow in length in response to regular stretching. Both these adaptations increase the range of movement possible about a joint. The range of movement about a joint is also affected by the joint structure and amount of sub-cutaneous fat.

1.8.3 ANTICIPATION OF MUSCLE LOADING

The muscle spindle can be set at a prescribed firing tension, feeding back sensory information when stretched beyond that certain tension. This pre-setting of muscle spindles is known as **gamma bias** and allows the detection of the stretching of a muscle at different degrees of its contraction. When wishing to maintain a muscle contraction of a certain tension, the gamma bias can be reset so that stretching of this now partially contracted muscle can be detected. An example is seen when one prepares to lift a load, the weight of which is anticipated as being 'heavy'.

❖ *Training and Performance Applications*

Anticipating the force of muscle action required under varying circumstances, plays a major role in sport participation. Consider for example the fine control exerted in racquet sports, such as tennis and squash. The ball approaches at a wide variety of speeds, and yet the return shot is invariably weighted correctly within very fine limits. In weight lifting, misjudgements leading to injury serve to highlight the protective function of correct anticipation. Although this is basically a reflex action, there is an element of conscious input into the process.

1.8.4 FINE CONTROL OF MUSCLE ACTION

Stimulation of skeletal muscle can either be direct via the **alpha** motor neurones which innervate the muscle fibres, or indirectly via the muscle spindles.

With indirect control via the muscle spindles, the **gamma** motor neurones stimulate the contractile ends of the intrafusal fibres within the muscle spindle, thus stretching the sensory stretch receptor endings in the centre. This stretching causes reflex contraction of the extra-fusal or normal muscle fibres via the alpha motor neurones.

Stimulation of muscle contraction via the muscle spindles takes longer than direct alpha motor fibre stimulation, as not only is the nerve pathway via the muscle spindle longer, but the gamma neurones have a smaller diameter and therefore conduct impulses more slowly than the alpha neurones. Activation via the gamma motor system can give finer control than direct alpha motor control, but if the gamma motor system is used whilst the muscle fibres are contracting under alpha motor stimulation *(alpha-gamma co-activation)*, then the muscle spindle reflex reinforces the muscle contraction, producing greater force.

Skeletal muscles typically occur in pairs, for example the biceps and triceps of the upper arm. The stimulation of a muscle to contract typically leads to the inhibition of the muscle that works in opposition to it *(reciprocal inhibition)*, so that it cannot contract at the same time and oppose the intended action. So in this example, if the biceps contracts, the triceps relaxes; and vice versa.

❖ *Training and Performance Applications*

Muscle co-ordination and reactions are improved by a proper 'warm-up' period, so that the reciprocal inhibition between antagonistic muscles operates more efficiently. If performers of explosive power events, such as sprinters, field event athletes, and games players, do not carry out such a 'warm-up' correctly (not to be confused with simple static stretching), then they are prone to muscle 'tears' and 'pulls', caused as a result of one of a pair of antagonistic muscles not relaxing quickly enough as the other one contracts. The classic example of this is the 'hamstring' injuries suffered by sprinters.

1.8.5 OTHER SENSORY RECEPTORS

Golgi tendon organs.

These occur at the junction of a tendon and its muscle. They detect the degree of stretch of the tendon. When stretched, they trigger the reflex inhibition of the contracting muscle that is causing the tendon to be stretched, and the reflex contraction of the antagonist *(reciprocal activation)*. This prevents damage to the muscle and tendon. Golgi tendon organs are less sensitive than muscle spindles, and only come into operation at high, potentially damaging tensions.

❖ *Training and Performance Applications*

It is thought that stretching may relieve muscular cramp as a result of the Golgi tendon organs sending inhibitory impulses to the muscle involved, causing it to relax. These protective reflexes of the tendon organs also operate more efficiently after a proper 'warm-up' period. If a muscle is stretched for longer than about six seconds, the Golgi tendon organs are activated, resulting in relaxation of the stretched muscle; this is known as the inverse stretch reflex as it opposes the stretch reflex.

If a limb is moved passively (i.e. with the assistance of a partner) to the limits of its range of movement and the muscles then contracted isometrically (without shortening) for about six seconds in that position, and then the muscles are relaxed; the limit of extension will be increased as a result of proprioceptive neuromuscular facilitation (PNF). That is the proprioceptors (muscle spindle apparatus and Golgi tendon organs), are facilitating (helping) stretching by means of neuromuscular events. In other words the passive stretch and the contracted muscle acting on the tendon result in the Golgi tendon organ causing further muscle relaxation, which helps further stretching; at the same time the muscle spindle apparatuses are habituated and any reflex contraction caused by the stretching is decreased.

Joint receptors.

These are sensory nerve endings found in the joint capsules and ligaments which detect movement and position of the joint.

Pain receptors.

Pain receptors are scattered throughout the muscle fibres, their connective tissue and blood vessels. Stimulation of these receptors is experienced as pain.

1.9 ANATOMY OF MOVEMENT

1.9.1 TYPES OF SKELETAL MUSCLES.

Muscle fibres are bound by connective tissue into bundles. Within these bundles the fibres are arranged parallel to the longitudinal axis. The bundles, however, are arranged within muscles in a variety of patterns. The pattern, along with the particular attachment of the muscle to the skeleton, determines the force and range of movement that can be produced

Fusiform muscles have comparatively few long bundles, arranged parallel with the longitudinal axis of the muscles, running into flat, strap-like tendons at each end. This arrangement allows the muscle to contract to its shortest, and they are attached in positions that can result in rapid and wide ranging movements. An example is seen in the biceps brachii which flexes the arm.

Pennate muscles are broad and flat with comparatively more, shorter bundles radiating out from a single tendon that extends the length of the muscle. Muscle fibres can contract to just over half of their resting length. Therefore the shorter fibres of pennate muscles cannot contract by as much as those of fusiform muscles, but as there are more of them, the pennate muscle can contract more forcefully. Pennate muscles are attached in positions that can result in powerful movements, for example the rectus femoris of the thigh, which straightens the leg at the knee.

1.9.2 TYPES OF MUSCLE ACTION

Muscles can act in a variety of ways with regard to changes in length and tension; and the interaction of this muscular force, the load, and the action of the bones as levers, determines the outcome.

Concentric actions

These are perhaps the most familiar types of contraction, in which the whole muscle shortens as it develops tension. There are different types of such action.

For example **Isotonic** contractions occur when, under constant load, the muscle shortens, with varying tensions over the range of movement about a joint. This type of contraction is seen for example in the biceps muscle of the arm when 'curling a weight'.

Figure 1.9: *Isotonic contraction*

Tension under constant load

Joint angle

Figure 1.10: *Isokinetic contraction*

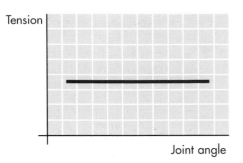

Tension

Joint angle

Figure1.11: *Major body axes and planes. To help the understanding of movement of segments of the body with respect to one another, imaginary reference planes are used. Within each plane an axis can be identified, usually in association with a particular joint, about which movement takes place.*

Isokinetic contractions occur when the muscle shortens at constant speed, and exerts maximum tension over the full range of movement at all joint angles. This is only fully achieved with specially designed weight training apparatus, which automatically adjusts the resistance over the full range of movement. The closest natural example of such isokinetic contraction in sport, is seen in the freestyle swimming armstroke.

Isometric actions occur when the muscle is prevented from shortening whilst it is generating tension, as for example when straining against an immovable resistance. Even though the bones involved may not be moving, initially the sliding filament mechanism operates as the 'slack' in the elastic soft tissues is taken up, but once the steady state is achieved the cross bridges of different fibres operate alternately to hold the filaments steady in one position.

Although classified separately in this way, isometric and isotonic contractions are both involved in the typical muscle contraction that results in movement; isometric contraction occurs initially before sufficient force is generated to actually start the movement, and isotonic contraction occurs once the movement is started.

Eccentric action.

Here the muscle develops its active tension whilst it is being lengthened by stretching. One example of this is seen in the quadriceps muscle at the front of the thigh when walking or running down steps or down hill. Another is seen in the biceps of the arms as they control the lowering of a weight after a curl.

❖ *Training and Performance Applications*

*A training method known as **plyometrics** uses both concentric and eccentric contractions. In plyometrics, maximum concentric effort is made immediately following an eccentric phase, in which the muscles have been stretched whilst developing tension. Muscles contract with greater force as a result of alpha (a) and gamma (g) co-activation. This is further reinforced by passive elastic recoil of the muscle, when the muscle is extended beyond its resting length, before being stimulated to contract. In this way muscles generate what can be referred to as explosive power. This is achieved for example by bounding and hopping, and is widely used by athletes wishing to increase their leg power.*

1.9.3 MOVEMENT IN RELATION TO THE MAJOR BODY PLANES AND AXES

Figure 1.12: *Movement in relation to the major body planes and axes.*

Voluntary muscles exert their action via the skeleton, which acts as a series of levers, articulated at joints, which allow movement in all planes.

Front

Front

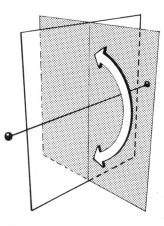

Front

(i) Side to side (transverse) axis, involved in movement in the sagittal plane known as **flexion** *and* **extension,** *e.g. bending (flexion) and straightening (extension) the arm at the elbow.*

(ii) Vertical axis, involved in movement in a transverse plane known as **rotation,** *e.g. rotating the head from side to side.*

(iii) Front to back axis, involved in movement in a frontal (coronal) plane known as **abduction** *and* **adduction,** *e.g. raising the arm sideways at the shoulder (abduction), and lowering it (adduction).*

1.9.4 MUSCLE ARRANGEMENTS

The muscles act in groups rather than singly, with most arranged in opposed or **antagonistic pairs** at joints, for example flexors and extensors. The muscle that causes the required action is called the prime mover or **agonist** *(protagonist)*, for example the biceps brachii flexing the arm at the elbow. At the same time the **antagonist** muscle, in this case the triceps brachii, is inhibited and relaxes, allowing the flexion to occur. If the arm is extended at the elbow, then the roles of agonist and antagonist are reversed, with the triceps brachii being the agonist, and the biceps brachii being the antagonist.

Muscles known as **fixators** or **stabilisers** hold or fix joints in a stable position, as for example when keeping the wrist stiff during a biceps curl with weights.

Others known as **synergists** prevent any unwanted movement and help the prime mover to function more efficiently.

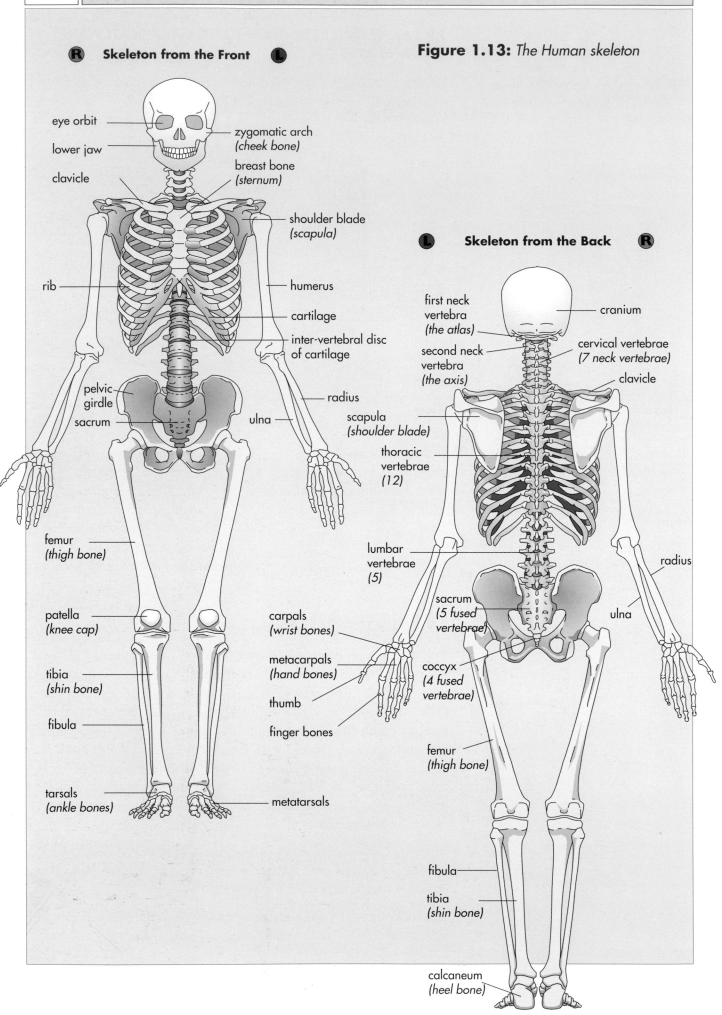

Ⓡ **Skeleton from the Front** Ⓛ

Figure 1.13: *The Human skeleton*

eye orbit

lower jaw

clavicle

zygomatic arch
(cheek bone)

breast bone
(sternum)

shoulder blade
(scapula)

rib

humerus

cartilage

inter-vertebral disc
of cartilage

pelvic
girdle

sacrum

radius

ulna

femur
(thigh bone)

patella
(knee cap)

tibia
(shin bone)

fibula

tarsals
(ankle bones)

carpals
(wrist bones)

metacarpals
(hand bones)

thumb

finger bones

metatarsals

Ⓛ **Skeleton from the Back** Ⓡ

first neck
vertebra
(the atlas)

second neck
vertebra
(the axis)

cranium

cervical vertebrae
(7 neck vertebrae)

clavicle

scapula
(shoulder blade)

thoracic
vertebrae
(12)

lumbar
vertebrae
(5)

sacrum
*(5 fused
vertebrae)*

coccyx
*(4 fused
vertebrae)*

radius

ulna

femur
(thigh bone)

fibula

tibia
(shin bone)

calcaneum
(heel bone)

Figure 1.14: *Superficial muscles of the human body. Not all muscles are shown and those that are have been simplified*

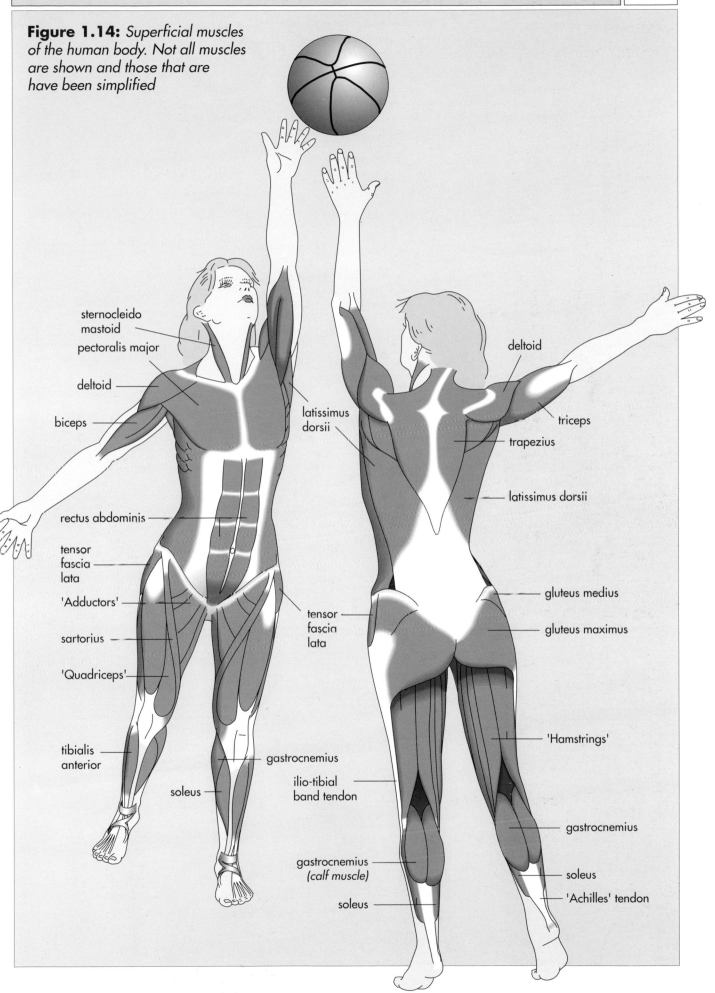

sternocleido mastoid

pectoralis major

deltoid

biceps

rectus abdominis

tensor fascia lata

'Adductors'

sartorius

'Quadriceps'

tibialis anterior

soleus

latissimus dorsii

tensor fascia lata

gastrocnemius

gastrocnemius (calf muscle)

soleus

ilio-tibial band tendon

deltoid

triceps

trapezius

latissimus dorsii

gluteus medius

gluteus maximus

'Hamstrings'

gastrocnemius

soleus

'Achilles' tendon

Figure 1.15: *Main types of movable joint*

Hinge joint
e.g. elbow joint between the humerus and the ulna and radius.

humerus

movement in one plane only i.e. only up and down

Axis of joint

ulna

radius

Pivot *(peg and socket)* **joint**
e.g joint between the atlas *(1st)* and the *axis (2nd)* vertebrae.

Axis of joint

atlas

transverse ligament

axis

bony peg of the axis

neural canal in which the spinal cord runs

Ball and socket joint
e.g. hip joint between the femur and the pelvic girdle.

Pelvic girdle

sacrum

femur

knee cap *(patella)*

Synovial joint structure
as seen in section of the hip joint.

muscle

tendon *(non-elastic)* attaching muscle to bone

synovial membrane

bursa or sac containing synovial fluid

joint capsular ligament *(elastic)* attaching bone to bone

pelvic girdle

head of femur

synovial fluid lubricates movement between, and supplies nutrients to, the articular cartilages

articular cartilage

Front View

Major Muscles of the Trunk

Lateral Flexion

Ⓡ   Ⓛ   Ⓡ   Ⓛ   Ⓛ   Ⓡ

rectus abdominis muscles on left side relaxed

erector spinae muscles on left side relaxed

rectus abdominis muscles on right side contracted

rectus abdominis muscles set in tendinous sheet (attached to sternum, rib cage and pelvic girdle)

erector spinae muscles on right side contracted

Back View

Ⓛ   Ⓡ

erector spinae muscles (attached to skull, vertebral column, ribs, and pelvic girdle)

Figure 1.16: *Major muscles used in the lateral flexion, forward flexion and hyperextension of the trunk*

Forward Flexion

Hyperextension

erector spinae muscles relaxed

rectus abdominis relaxed

rectus abdominis muscles contracted

when standing up straight the erector spinae muscles are contracted, they contract even more to bend spine backwards

Major Muscles of the Upper Body

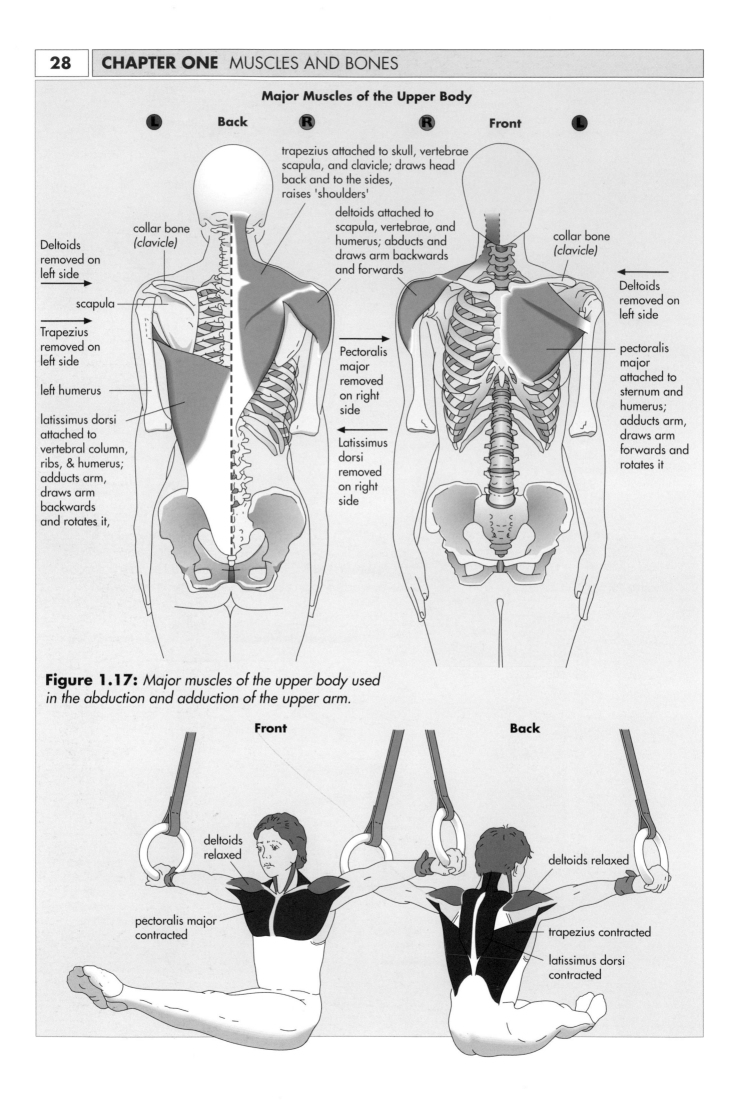

L **Back** **R**   **R** **Front** **L**

trapezius attached to skull, vertebrae scapula, and clavicle; draws head back and to the sides, raises 'shoulders'

deltoids attached to scapula, vertebrae, and humerus; abducts and draws arm backwards and forwards

collar bone *(clavicle)*

Deltoids removed on left side

scapula

Trapezius removed on left side

left humerus

latissimus dorsi attached to vertebral column, ribs, & humerus; adducts arm, draws arm backwards and rotates it,

Pectoralis major removed on right side

Latissimus dorsi removed on right side

collar bone *(clavicle)*

Deltoids removed on left side

pectoralis major attached to sternum and humerus; adducts arm, draws arm forwards and rotates it

Figure 1.17: *Major muscles of the upper body used in the abduction and adduction of the upper arm.*

Front **Back**

deltoids relaxed

pectoralis major contracted

deltoids relaxed

trapezius contracted

latissimus dorsi contracted

Extension
Right arm viewed from the side

origin tendons

triceps contracted to extend elbow

biceps relaxed

humerus

insertion tendon

ulna

radius

Flexion
Right arm viewed from the side

scapula

biceps contracted to flex elbow and supinate forearm and hand

triceps relaxed

radius

humerus

ulna

Supination (Palm up)

biceps contracted

pronator teres relaxed

Palm up

Palm up

Pronation (Palm down)

biceps relaxed

pronator teres contracted

Palm down

Palm down

Figure 1.18: *Major muscles used in the extension, flexion, supination and pronation of the arm*

Front View

(R)   (L)

tensor
fascia
lata

sartorius
attached to
pelvic girdle
and tibia;
contracts to
flex hip
and knee,
and rotate the leg

ilio-tibial band
of fascia
running from
pelvic girdle to
tibia

'knee cap'
(patella)

extensor digitorum
longus attached to
fibula and 'small toes'

'adductors'

'Quadriceps'
a group of
four muscles
attached to
pelvic girdle,
patella (knee cap),
and tibia;
contracts to
extend knee
and flex hip

'Hamstrings'

gastrocnemius
attached to femur
and heel bone

tibialis anterior
attached to tibia
and underside
of 'big toe'

soleus
attached to fibula
and heel bone

'Achilles' tendon

Side View

gluteus medius

gluteus
maximus
attached to
pelvic girdle
and femur

tensor
fascia
lata

fascia
lata

ilio-tibial band

'Quadriceps'
rectus femoris
vastus lateralis
in view

'knee cap'
(patella)

head of fibula
origin for
soleus and
extensor
digitorum
longus

shin bone
(tibia)

fibula

Right leg seen from the right

Figure 1.19: *Major muscles used in the leg
for extension and flexing of the hip and knee.*

gluteus maximus
contracts to extend hip

'Hamstrings'
contract to extend hip
and flex knee

'Quadriceps'
contract to flex hip
and extend knee

'Hamstrings'
relaxed

'Quadriceps'
relaxed

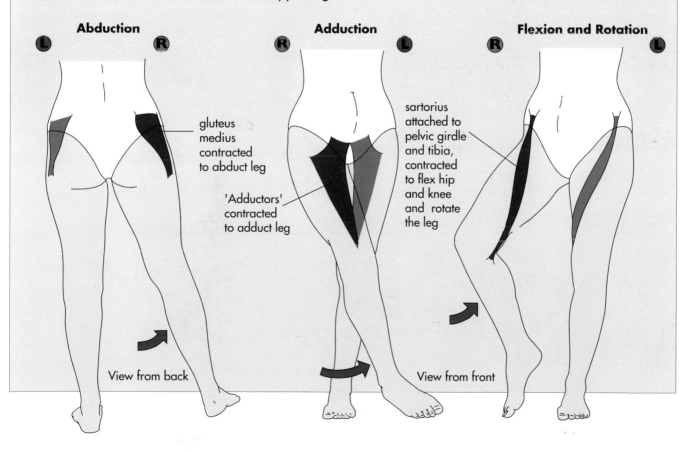

View from Back

Ⓛ Ⓡ

gluteus maximus attached to pelvic girdle and femur (covering gluteus medius)

'Hamstring' muscles - group of three muscles attached to pelvic girdle, femur, tibia, and fibula - contract to extend hip and flex knee

gluteus maximus removed to show gluteus medius attached to pelvic girdle and top of femur

hip joint

'Adductors' a group of muscles attached to pelvic girdle and upper femur

gracilis attached to pelvic girdle and tibia contracts to adduct and rotate femur

femur

tibia

fibula

View from Front

Ⓡ Ⓛ

superficial adductors removed to reveal the adductor magnus

Figure 1.20: *Major muscles used, in abduction, adduction, flexion and rotation of the upper leg.*

Abduction

Ⓛ Ⓡ

gluteus medius contracted to abduct leg

'Adductors' contracted to adduct leg

View from back

Adduction

Ⓡ Ⓛ

sartorius attached to pelvic girdle and tibia, contracted to flex hip and knee and rotate the leg

View from front

Flexion and Rotation

Ⓡ Ⓛ

Lower Leg Muscles Front View

Ⓡ Ⓛ

Eversion (pronation)

Normal Stance

Inversion (supination)

extensor digitorum longus contracts to pronate (evert) foot

tibialis anterior attached to tibia and underside of 'big toe'

extensor digitorum longus attached to fibula and 'small toes'

extensor digitorum longus

tibialis anterior

tibialis anterior contracts to supinate (invert) foot

Right leg seen from front

Figure 1.21: *Major muscles of the lower leg, used in pronation, supination, dorsi-flexion, and plantar-flexion of the foot.*

Lower Leg muscles Back View

Ⓡ Ⓛ

Dorsi-flexion of Foot

Plantar-flexion of Foot

gastrocnemius removed to reveal soleus attached to head of fibula and heel bone

tibialis anterior and extensor digitorum longus contract to give dorsi-flexion of foot

calf muscle (gastrocnemius) attached to femur and heel bone

soleus

'Achilles' tendon

gastrocnemius relaxed

foot muscles relaxed

gastrocnemius contracts to give plantar flexion of foot

tibialis anterior and extensor digitorum longus relaxed

foot muscles contract to contribute to plantar flexion of foot

Left leg seen from outside

Table: 1.5: *Major muscles and their actions*

MUSCLE.	ACTION.	EXERCISE.
Adductor longus.	Adducts and rotates leg.	Forcing legs together.
Biceps brachii.	Flexes elbow. Adducts arm Supinates forearm & hand.	Curling, chinning.
Deltoids.	Raise arm to shoulder level. Helps overhead movement.	Forward, lateral & back arm raises, overhead lifting.
Erector spinae.	Holds spine erect *(extension)*	Standing up straight, raising arms and shoulders while lying prone *(on front)*
Gastrocnemius.	Plantar flexion of foot, helps flex knee.	Rising onto tiptoe, as in running and jumping.
Gluteus maximus..	Extends thigh & rotates it outwards.	Knee bending movements ie. squats, stair climbing, cycling.
'Hamstrings'	A group of muscles which flex knee & extend hip.	Extending leg behind & flexing knee as in running.
Latissimus dorsi.	Pulls arm downwards & backwards. Depresses shoulder girdle, bends trunk sideways.	Pull downs behind head, pressing movements.
Pectoralis major.	Pulls arm forwards & inwards.	All pressing movements.
Quadriceps femoris	A group of muscles which extends knee & flexes hip.	Knee bends, leg raises.
Rectus abdominis.	Flexion & lateral flexion of trunk.	Sit ups, side bends, leg raises.
Sartorius.	Flexes knee, flexes hip & rotates thigh outwards.	Crossing legs whilst seated.
Soleus.	Plantar flexion of foot.	Rising on tiptoe.
Sternocleido-mastoid.	Pulls head forward & to side, rotates it.	Forward bridging, pushing on forehead.
Tibialis anterior	Dorsi-flexion, adduction & inversion of foot.	Running.
Trapezius.	Draws head back & to sides, raises shoulders.	Shrugging, & all lifting overhead.
Triceps brachii.	Extends elbow & draws it back.	Press ups, dips, all over head lifting.

2.1.1 GLYCEROL AND FREE FATTY ACIDS

The glycerol and free fatty acids *(FFAs)* may be used directly as a source of energy, or resynthesised into fats and stored in the fatty *(adipose)* tissue which contain as much as 98% of the body's total energy reserves. Glycerol *(but not FFAs)* can be converted into glucose. This is particularly important when the diet is low in carbohydrates, and during endurance exercise which depletes the glycogen reserves.

2.1.2 GLUCOSE

Some of the glucose may be used directly from the blood plasma, and any glucose in excess of the normal levels in the blood is converted either into the insoluble storage carbohydrate glycogen in the muscles and the liver, or into fat which is stored in specialised adipose tissue under the skin, and around the major organs of the body.

2.1.3 AMINO ACIDS

The amino acids also circulate in the plasma, and are mainly used to synthesise proteins for growth and repair throughout the body. Excess amino acids cannot be stored in the body, so they are deaminated in the liver, a process in which their nitrogen containing amino groups are removed, producing toxic nitrogen containing waste products such as urea. Whilst exercising, the urea excreted in the sweat exceeds that excreted by the kidneys, which have a reduced blood supply during exercise. The remainders of the now deaminated amino acid molecules, can either be used directly in the respiratory pathways, or be converted into glucose.

2.1.4 INTERCONVERSIONS OF ENERGY SOURCES

All these fuels are to a certain extent interconvertible, depending on their relative supplies, and the particular demands of the body at any one time. The liver is the main centre for these interconversions, and for maintaining constant optimum *(homeostatic)* levels in the blood. Theoretically most of these interconversions are reversible, but this is not always true in practice. Thus although the liver can convert excess glucose more readily into fats than into glycogen, very little glucose, if any, can be produced from fats. Also, although liver glycogen is readily converted into blood glucose, muscle glycogen is not.

2.2 USE OF ENERGY SOURCES IN EXERCISE

At rest, about two thirds of the energy required for the body is derived from fats, and one third from the carbohydrates glycogen and glucose. The relative amounts of these fuels used in exercise depends on many factors; including the type of exercise *(whether it is intermittent or continuous, short or long, light or heavy)*, the types of muscle fibre involved, the nature of the diet, and the state of physical training - which in turn determines the supply of oxygen.

2.2.1 FATS

The complete oxidation of fats depends on the presence of oxygen, so the relative contribution of fat to the energy demands of the body is largely determined by the supply of oxygen to the tissues. In the long term functioning of slow twitch muscle fibres, fat is the main energy source under aerobic conditions, so that after about an hour of continuous aerobic exercise the majority of the energy is derived from fats. Training increases the capacity for oxygen uptake, and therefore increases the ability to use fats.

Very little fat is stored in the muscle fibres, therefore the fatty acids and glycerol must be supplied via the bloodstream. The adipose tissue releases free fatty acids *(FFAs)* into the plasma of the blood, which are transported to the muscles loosely bound to plasma proteins. Those who take part in regular aerobic endurance work increase their ability to release fatty acids from their fat stores, and can therefore use more fats as an energy source during exercise

The glycerol from the breakdown of fats can either enter the carbohydrate respiratory pathways directly, or be converted into glucose which is then broken down in the normal way.

Fats tightly bound to proteins, known as lipoproteins are also transported in the plasma. These originate from dietary fats absorbed in the small intestine. They are carried to the liver where they are converted to two different types of lipoprotein, low density lipoproteins *(LDLs)* which supply cholesterol to the tissues, and high density lipoproteins *(HDLs)* which remove cholesterol from the tissues. Exercise tends to increase the ratio of HDLs to LDLs , which seems to be a factor in lowering the risk of atherosclerosis *(the formation of fatty deposits or plaques on the walls of blood vessels)*. Their exact role in the energy economy of the tissues is not fully understood, but the enzyme lipoprotein lipase, which is attached to the surface of the cells lining the capillaries supplying the muscles, releases FFAs from these circulating lipoproteins, making them available to the working muscles.

2.2.2 CARBOHYDRATES

Glycogen within the muscle fibres is available for immediate use, for example at the onset of exercise and/or during intense exercise. During these periods, the supply of oxygen is usually insufficient for the complete aerobic oxidation of carbohydrates and fats. Only carbohydrates can be broken down anaerobically to maintain the supply of energy to the contracting muscle fibres.

❖ *Training and Performance Applications*

Generally speaking, as the intensity of the exercise increases there is an increase in the use of carbohydrates as an energy source, so that they become the main fuel at about 50 - 70% of the maximum oxygen uptake ($\dot{V}_{O_2}$ max). Elite marathon runners can perform at more than 80% of their maximum oxygen uptake and therefore use mainly glycogen, even though they are performing what would normally be considered as endurance exercise mainly exploiting fat.

The anaerobic breakdown of carbohydrates *(anaerobic glycolysis)* results in the production of lactic acid *(Section 2.5.2, p 48)*. The increased acidity *(decrease in pH)* inhibits the mobilisation of FFAs and subsequently interferes with their use, further emphasising the importance of the muscle glycogen stores as an energy source during intense activity.

When oxygen supplies are sufficient, the use of carbohydrates as a fuel has another advantage, that is, for a given volume of oxygen, carbohydrates yield about 12% more energy than fat.

Carbohydrate Stores

The total carbohydrate store in the body is about 375-475 g; of which up to 345 g are stored as muscle glycogen, 90-110 g are stored as liver glycogen, and 15-20 g are found in the plasma as blood glucose. Active muscle fibres can use glucose obtained from all these sources. However, blood glucose is the only source of energy for the brain, and most of the glucose released from the liver glycogen stores is used for this purpose.

The main disadvantage of using glycogen is that stores are very limited when compared with fat, and they can be depleted relatively quickly within a few hours. The depletion of muscle glycogen stores leads rapidly to muscular fatigue. This is why the use of fat is of such importance the longer exercise continues.

During the recovery period there is a rapid replenishment of glycogen within the first few hours, which is quicker in the fast twitch than in the slow twitch muscle fibres. After this, it can take two or more days for it to be restored fully to its pre-exercise levels.

❖ *Training and Performance Applications*

Glycogen stores can be increased to higher levels than normal by special dietary and exercise regimes. This process of glycogen 'loading' or 'supercompensation' can help extend the period of endurance exercise before the onset of fatigue. The technique is based on the principle that if glycogen stores are depleted, and held at a low level for a few days, either by restricting the intake of carbohydrates and/or continuing to exercise, then when carbohydrates are readily available once again in the diet, the body overcompensates and increases its stores of glycogen above the normal level. However, problems can arise with the technique. It is not always successful, declines in effectiveness with repeated use, and may even disrupt normal performance. The rapid increase in weight associated with glycogen loading, is due to the volume of water that is associated with the stored glycogen.

Maintenance of Blood Glucose Levels

If the blood glucose levels begin to fall, brain function is interfered with. Therefore there are safeguards that prevent the muscles from using blood glucose too readily. For example, the ability of the muscles to absorb glucose from the blood is decreased by the reduction in the level of insulin in the blood, which occurs if the blood glucose falls. Therefore, if blood glucose begins to fall, the muscle fibres are decreasingly able to take up glucose and use it as an energy source. Therefore muscles will use glucose from their own glycogen stores, rather than from the plasma.

❖ *Training and Performance Applications*

During prolonged exercise, as muscle glycogen is depleted, exercising muscles do increasingly use blood glucose. A variety of homeostatic or steady state mechanisms, most of which are centred on the liver, operate to maintain blood glucose at optimum levels for as long as possible. For example as exercise proceeds, breakdown of liver glycogen releases glucose into the blood plasma. As the liver glycogen is depleted, glucose is increasingly made from new sources by the liver (gluconeogenesis) stimulated by the hormone glucagon. This 'new glucose' can be produced from glycerol (from fats), and/or from amino acids derived from proteins (particularly alanine, which may come from the breakdown of muscle protein itself). Eventually, if the use of glucose by the muscles and the brain becomes greater than the supply from the liver, the blood glucose level will gradually drop (hypoglycaemia), causing fatigue and a decrease in the normal functions of the brain. This is illustrated by the fact that athletes can have great difficulty in making the simplest of calculations in the last few miles of a Marathon.

During exercise, the taking in of glucose does not necessarily help. Concentrated solutions remain in the stomach and do not pass readily into the small intestine, where most absorption of water and glucose into the blood takes place under these conditions. Also, if the solution is too concentrated, even if it does pass into the small intestine absorption of water is reduced and in fact water will tend to be drawn out of the blood by osmosis. However, the absorption of water into the blood is increased if the solution of glucose is the same concentration as the blood (isotonic), this in fact is the main role of such isotonic drinks, rather than energy replacement. During endurance exercise, the problems associated with the intake of energy and water may be overcome by the use of a solution of long chain carbohydrate molecules (maltodextrins), obtained from the partial breakdown of starch. This does not slow the rate of stomach emptying, nor does it oppose the uptake of water in the small intestine, or trigger the release of insulin (Section 2.3), and it provides energy.

2.2.3 PROTEINS

It is estimated that up to about 10% of the energy used in exercise may be derived from proteins. There are several pathways by which this can occur.

Amino acids excess to requirements for protein synthesis can have their amino groups removed *(deamination)* in the liver, these amino groups produce urea, and the remainders of the molecules are broken down in respiration with the release of energy, or resynthesised into glucose and/or glycogen.

As the intensity of exercise increases, protein in the muscles is broken down into amino acids, and the amino acid alanine is increasingly released from the exercising muscles into the blood. The alanine is transported in the blood plasma to the liver, where it is deaminated *(producing urea)* and the residue is converted to glucose, which can then return to the exercising muscles, or be used to replenish liver glycogen stores. In this way muscle protein can be used as an energy source.

2.3 HORMONAL REGULATION OF ENERGY METABOLISM

Hormones are 'chemical messengers' secreted by ductless *(endocrine)* glands directly into the blood stream. They control or influence all aspects of metabolism. With respect to energy metabolism five hormones are mainly involved.

Adrenaline, noradrenaline and **glucagon** stimulate the conversion of glycogen to glucose, and together with **growth hormone** they stimulate the conversion of fats to FFAs and glycerol. These hormones also increase the activity of the enzyme lipoprotein lipase which increases the rate of supply of fatty acids. An increase in the secretion of these hormones will therefore increase the availability of energy for exercise.

Insulin inhibits the effects of adrenaline, and glucagon, and also inhibits the enzyme lipase which catalyses the breakdown of fats into FFAs and glycerol. An increase in the secretion of insulin will therefore decrease the availability of energy for exercise. An anabolic or protein building effect is also claimed for insulin, and some power athletes attempt to maintain raised insulin levels by continuous carbohydrate 'snacking' during workouts.

❖ *Training and Performance Applications*

It has been suggested that consuming sugars within an hour of starting exercise could be counterproductive, as the secretion of insulin would be stimulated, and the available energy for exercise therefore decreased. However, in practice this does not appear to be the case. Once the activity has started, the likelihood of any insulin reaction that might occur decreases, as a result of noradrenaline supressing insulin activity; and there is certainly an advantage to be gained by taking a certain amount of 'sugars' during the activity, not only as a source of energy but also to aid the uptake of water by the gut.

2.4 ENERGY SUPPLY SYSTEMS

There are three systems involved in supplying energy to the working muscles. The **alactic anaerobic** system or **phosphagen** system, the **lactic anaerobic** system, and the **aerobic** system. Each of these is suited to a particular type of exercise, and each can be improved by fairly specific training regimes. However, there is also extensive overlap between the systems which share common metabolic pathways.

The end product of all the energy releasing processes of cellular respiration is the energy rich compound adenosine triphosphate or **ATP**. ATP is the universal energy currency of all living things. It is the form in which energy is supplied for all purposes. Each molecule contains three phosphate groups, the end one of which can be more easily displaced than the others, with energy being made available for use by the muscle fibres. In this process, adenosine diphosphate *(ADP)* and a free phosphate group *(P)* are formed. This process is reversible, and energy released from the oxidation of energy rich materials can be trapped in the ATP molecule when a phosphate group is combined with ADP to reform ATP.

$$\text{A-P-P-P} \rightleftharpoons \text{A-P-P} + \text{P} + \text{Energy}$$
$$\text{(ATP)} \qquad \text{(ADP)}$$

The relative amounts of ATP and ADP + P control the rate of breakdown of energy rich substances in respiration. If ADP and P are present, then energy is required to synthesise ATP, and the rate of respiration increases to supply this energy. On the other hand, if there is only ATP present, there is no immediate demand for energy, and the rate of respiration decreases.

2.4.1 SOURCES OF ENERGY FOR THE REGENERATION OF ATP

There is a only a limited store of ATP within the muscle fibres, and as all energy used by the body must be channelled through ATP, it must be replenished as soon as it is used up. To ensure its rapid regeneration there is another energy rich phosphate compound in the muscles, namely phosphocreatine *(PC)*, which acts as the most immediate energy reserve for the resynthesis of ATP. The rapid availability is particularly important in fuelling contractions of high power.

$$\text{ADP} + \text{Phosphocreatine } (PC) \longrightarrow \text{ATP} + \text{Creatine } (C)$$

Oxygen is not directly used and no lactic acid is produced in the process, therefore it is referred to as the **alactic anaerobic** phase

PC in turn can only be regenerated using energy from ATP. Therefore, during maximal exercise, PC cannot be replenished, as the ATP is being used continuously in muscle contraction. However, it can be replenished within a few minutes after such exercise stops, when ATP becomes available again after having been regenerated via other pathways.

Figure 2.1: *Energy flow through ATP and PC (Phosphagen system).*

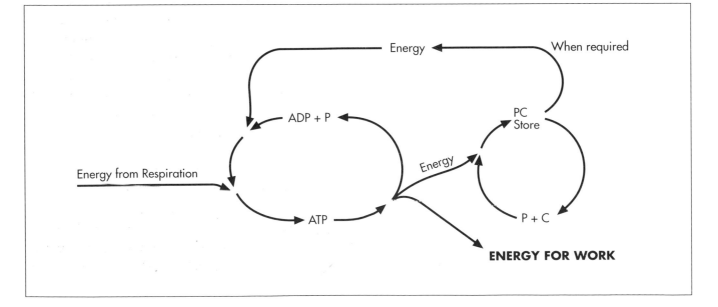

❖ *Training and Performance Applications*

This ATP/PC or phosphagen system provides enough energy at a sufficient rate for up to 6-10 seconds of flat out effort, as for example in the 100 metres sprint with most of the ATP being depleted within the first few seconds. After such effort the PC stores are depleting, and represent the limiting factor for muscle contraction during short term exercise. The phosphagen system is also of major importance in games playing, which involves repeated short bursts of intense activity, with periods of recovery in between. Training has no effect on the total amount of ATP available, but the amount of PC can be increased substantially by speed training. This has the effect of delaying the onset of the use of the lactic anaerobic system to regenerate the ATP, in other words the alactic/lactic threshold is raised. This means that the reduction in power output associated with the switch from the rapidly available energy of stored ATP/PC, to the indirect (and potentially more fatigueing) regeneration from lactic anaerobic pathways, is delayed. Taking about 20 g of creatine a day (as 4-5 g doses) for 5 days, increases the total muscle creatine content. If sub-maximal exercise is maintained during supplementation, muscle uptake can be further increased up to a certain saturation limit. Any increased intake past this point leads to excess being excreted by the kidneys. The increase in total muscle creatine of about 20% results in a significant increase in the amount of work which can be performed close to the maximum. It also results in a quicker recovery rate after exercise.

Although PC is always used to some extent at the beginning of any type of exercise to regenerate ATP, ATP is regenerated from other sources as well.

If the exercise is of the speed endurance type, energy from lactic anaerobic respiration *(in which lactic acid is generated)* is mainly used to regenerate the ATP.

If the exercise is of the endurance type, where the oxygen delivery systems become capable of sustaining aerobic respiration *(as a result of an increase in the breathing and heart rates)*, more energy from the aerobic oxidation of glycogen, FFA and blood glucose is used as the slow twitch muscle fibres become more involved. With this system a steady state can be reached, in which ATP is regenerated at the same rate as it is broken down, and performance can be maintained for long periods.

❖ *Training and Performance Applications*

All three components of the energy supply system, the alactic anaerobic, the lactic anaerobic, and the aerobic, are employed from the outset of any event involving continuous movement, but to varying degrees. For example, in a hard run 800 metres race, the alactic anaerobic system will fuel the quick kick off from the start. The lactic anaerobic system will be mainly used in the first 200-400 metres, which is the fastest phase of the race when demand for oxygen is greater than the supply. At the bell the runners gather themselves for the final lap, and by now the respiratory/circulatory systems have had time to adjust to the demands being made, so that aerobic respiration can increasingly operate. In the final kick for home over the last 200 metres, demand for oxygen again exceeds supply and the lactic anaerobic system floods the body with lactic acid, bringing the athlete to a virtual standstill at the end of the race, hopefully just past the finish line.

During exercise some ATP can also be regenerated from the combination of ADP molecules:

ADP + ADP $\rightleftharpoons$ ATP + AMP (Adenosine Monophosphate)

AMP activates respiratory enzymes, and stimulates the secretion of adrenaline, both of which increase the rate of respiration and therefore the regeneration of ATP from aerobic sources.

It is important to note that all these ways of resynthesising ATP may operate at the same time, but the relative importance of each one depends upon the activity and its duration.

2.5 METABOLIC PATHWAYS

The energy that is trapped and stored in the phosphagen system originates from the energy rich respiratory substrates. It is released from the energy rich sources by a series of enzyme catalysed reactions. In these metabolic pathways the respiratory substrates are oxidised to carbon dioxide and water, in the process known as cellular respiration. The breakdown of the different respiratory substrates involves common pathways.

The main pathway is that of the breakdown of carbohydrates, with the breakdown of fats and proteins linking in at different points.

❖ *Training and Performance Applications*

The complete oxidation of fats is dependent on carbohydrate breakdown. A certain level of carbohydrate breakdown is necessary to supply intermediate molecules necessary for the complete breakdown of fats. This situation is summarised in the phrase that 'fats only burn in the flames of carbohydrates'. In the absence of sufficient carbohydrate breakdown, as can arise when the glycogen reserves are depleted after about two hours of continuous exercise, the incomplete breakdown of fats can result in toxic ketosis, which causes breathlessness and vomiting. The depletion of glycogen reserves is the explanation of the experience of 'hitting the wall' in endurance events such as the Marathon. In the Marathon (26.2 miles, 41.9 kilometres), it is said that when you reach 20 miles (32 k) you are only half way. Physiologically and psychologically this statement has an element of truth!

*The ingestion of **caffeine** increases the plasma levels of FFAs and the ability of the muscles to use them, and consequently spares glycogen. Caffeine stimulates the nervous system increasing alertness and reducing feelings of pain and fatigue, and also increases the heart rate and ventilation rate. All these effects have implications for sport performance, and although a common ingredient of modern diets (coffee, tea, cocoa, chocolate, and colas) caffeine above a certain level is on the list of banned substances, where doping is defined as " the administration or use of substances in any form alien to the body, or of physiological substances in abnormal amounts and/or by abnormal methods by healthy persons with the exclusive aim of attaining an artificial and unfair increase in performance in sports." Caffeine is banned at a level equivalent to the consumption of 8 strong cups of percolated coffee or 10 cups of strong tea in two hours. Adverse effects include loss of water as a result of increased urine production, anxiety, insomnia, nausea, diarrhoea, headaches, irregular heart beats and raised blood pressure. There is no convincing evidence that it improves endurance performance significantly, but its misuse goes along way back with athletes of old chewing raw coffee beans before events.*

2.5.1 ANAEROBIC GLYCOLYSIS

The initial stages in the breakdown of carbohydrates occur in the cytoplasm of all cells, including muscle fibres. During these initial stages, energy is transferred directly from the substrate into ATP. Oxygen is not involved in these initial stages in the cytoplasm and they are therefore referred to as anaerobic glycolysis. Anaerobic glycolysis generates a net gain of two ATP molecules from each molecule of glucose, which only represents about 5% of the total ATP that can be generated from the complete breakdown of the glucose molecule. However, this process is important in supplying ATP in high intensity short term exercise, especially in fast twitch muscle fibres, as it supplies ATP more than twice as quickly as the aerobic system.

An essential part of these stages of anaerobic glycolysis, is the removal of hydrogen atoms from the substrate *(in a process known as oxidation)*. This hydrogen is accepted by the co-enzyme NAD, which is thus reduced to NAD2H *(NAD with two hydrogen atoms)*. For anaerobic glycolysis to continue, unreduced NAD must be regenerated by the removal of the 2H *(oxidation)* from the NAD2H. This is achieved in different ways depending on the availability of oxygen.

2.5.2 LACTIC ACID METABOLISM

When the demand of the muscles for oxygen exceeds the supply, as for example at the beginning of most types of exercise, but particularly during intense efforts lasting up to about a minute, an intermediate product (pyruvic acid) of the breakdown of glucose, is used to oxidise the NAD2H. In doing this, the pyruvic acid itself becomes reduced to lactic acid. The complete breakdown of glucose is thus prevented, as an intermediate product of the breakdown of glucose is being used to form lactic acid, instead of going on to be oxidised to carbon dioxide and water with the release of much larger amounts of energy in the mitochondria.

A small amount of lactic acid is formed even during the lightest exercise, but if its rate of removal is less than or equal to its rate of production it does not accumulate. When the rate of production does exceed its rate of removal, lactic acid begins to accumulate in the blood. There are normally about 1-2 millimoles of lactic acid per dm^3 (litre) of blood, and it is generally agreed that a level of 4 millimoles per dm^3 (litre) of blood represents what has been called the 'anaerobic threshold'. However, this term is misleading, as anaerobic respiration occurs from the very start of exercise to a greater or lesser extent, with no clear 'threshold' as such, therefore the term **Onset of Blood Lactate Accumulation** *(OBLA)* is to be preferred. Not all of the OBLA is due to an increase in lactic acid production however, a proportion results from less lactic acid than normal being removed from the blood by the liver, as blood is shunted away from the liver during exercise. OBLA occurs at a certain percentage of the aerobic capacity *(normally between 50-60% in untrained subjects.)* In other words, the closer one is to the maximum aerobic capacity, the more anaerobic respiration will be going on. If the rate of oxygen uptake comes to match the requirement for aerobic respiration during exercise, a 'steady state' exists, and the lactic acid level in the blood remains relatively constant until the end of the exercise.

❖ *Training and Performance Applications*

OBLA occurs at a higher percentage of aerobic capacity in trained subjects, as they have an increased rate of lactic acid removal, and therefore it accumulates more slowly. However, in addition, trained subjects can also tolerate much higher levels of blood lactate than untrained subjects. The effect of the accumulating lactic acid is to increase fatigue, and to increase the rate of breathing eventually even past the point at which any extra oxygen uptake can be achieved. It is around the start of this process of lactic acid build up during exercise that conversations tend to stop! It is the accumulation of lactic acid that makes the 400 m 'sprint' such a testing event. One effect of training for such high intensity events is to condition the tissues and nervous system to tolerate the high levels of lactic acid produced during the lactic anaerobic phase.

There are several ways by which lactic acid can be removed from the muscles. Some of them are of relatively minor importance, namely its loss in sweat and urine, and its reconversion to glycogen in the liver and in the muscles. This reconversion to glycogen in fact requires more energy than was yielded by the original anaerobic glycolysis, so that there is no overall gain of energy if this occurs.

The major pathway for the removal of lactic acid is its aerobic oxidation to carbon dioxide and water, yielding ATP. This can occur in the muscle fibres themselves once sufficient oxygen is available, especially in the slow twitch fibres of muscles not taking part in the acute exercise. Or the lactic acid can be transported in the blood to organs which are not operating under anaerobic conditions, where it can be oxidised, for example the heart, brain, liver, and kidneys. As it can be used in this way it is not therefore a waste product as such.

2.5.3 AEROBIC PATHWAYS

If sufficient oxygen is delivered to the working muscles it can be used to re-oxidise the NAD2H produced in the oxidation of glucose to pyruvic acid. As described before, this results in the production of water and the regeneration of the NAD. Therefore, instead of being converted to lactic acid, the pyruvic acid is free to continue down the metabolic pathway that leads to its complete oxidation into carbon dioxide and water, and the production of many more molecules of ATP.

These aerobic stages take place in the cell structures or organelles known as mitochondria. Slow twitch muscle fibres have large numbers of mitochondria containing the enzymes, coenzymes, and cytochrome pigments necessary for the aerobic stages. All of these are increased as a result of aerobic training.

The complete oxidation of pyruvic acid occurs via a cyclic process known as the Krebs Cycle which produces more NAD2H. This NAD2H is oxidised back to NAD by the removal of hydrogen atoms, which are subsequently oxidised by oxygen, producing water, and releasing energy which is trapped in ATP.

This complete oxidation of a glucose molecule results in the production of 38 molecules of ATP

Figure 2.2: *Diagram of metabolic pathways involved in energy release from glycogen and glucose during and immediately after. exercise*

Glycogen Reserves
in Muscles

Converted to
Glucose

Glucose

Oxidation of Glucose
by the removal
of Hydrogen

If insufficient
Oxygen available

2 ATP gained for
every Molecule of
Glucose broken down
to Pyruvic Acid

Pyruvic Acid

Lactic Acid
accumulates

If sufficient
Oxygen available

Reactions above dotted line
occur in Cytoplasm

Reactions below dotted line
occur in Mitochondria

H_2O

Krebs Cycle of
Reactions

CO_2

38 ATP Gained for
every Molecule of
Glucose Oxidised

Summary Equation

$$C_6H_{12}O_6 + 6O_2 \rightarrow 6CO_2 + 6H_2O + 38 \text{ ATP}$$

Figure 2.3: *Relationship of energy systems utilised over a one mile race in a top class performance.*

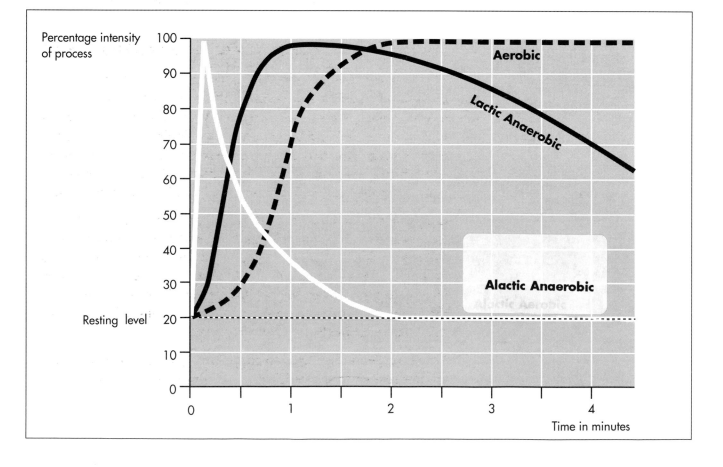

2.6 OXYGEN REQUIREMENT FOR ENERGY RELEASE

2.6.1 OXYGEN DEFICIT

The oxygen deficit is defined as: the difference between, the calculated amount of oxygen necessary to supply the energy *(from aerobic respiration)* for the work during a period of exercise *(therefore removing the need for any anaerobic respiration)*, and the actual amount of oxygen absorbed during the exercise period in excess of that which would have been absorbed in an equivalent period of rest. In other words, the amount of oxygen that the subject was short of during the exercise.

2.6.2 OXYGEN DEBT

During recovery from exercise, the oxygen consumption remains high, above the rate of consumption for an equivalent period of rest. Originally this amount of extra oxygen required during recovery, was assumed to be that which was needed for the removal of the accumulated lactic acid *(most of which was thought to be resynthesised to glycogen)*, and was therefore referred to as the 'oxygen debt'. However, there is only a slight relationship between the oxygen deficit and the so-called 'oxygen debt'; with the 'oxygen debt' being up to twice the oxygen deficit. In other words the 'oxygen debt' is not simply involved with the repayment of a deficit incurred during exercise. Therefore a better term is the **excess post - exercise oxygen consumption** *(EPOC)*.

2.6.3 EXCESS POST EXERCISE OXYGEN CONSUMPTION (EPOC)

There are two components to the EPOC, namely the **fast** component and the **slow** component. In the fast component, the oxygen consumed is used to regenerate the phosphagen system of ATP and PC, and to resaturate the myoglobin and tissue fluids with oxygen. This part has been referred to as the **alactic 'debt'** or **alactic recovery oxygen consumption**. If the exercise was mainly aerobic this would be replaced within several minutes.

In recovery from more strenuous exercise, which has resulted in the production of lactic acid, and raised the body temperature, there is an additional slow component, and it may be as long as 24 hours after stopping exercise before the oxygen consumption returns to pre-exercise levels. This slower phase is referred to as the **lactic 'debt'** or **lactic recovery oxygen consumption**, as it is in this phase that the lactic acid is removed.

Much oxygen is also used to supply many other processes which are not related to the deficit incurred during exercise. Oxygen is needed to supply the muscles of the thorax *(chest)* responsible for the increased breathing rate, and the more rapid beating of the heart, and also to maintain the higher metabolic rate due to the raised body temperature and the residual effects of the hormones adrenaline and thyroxine. The redistribution of ions *(such as calcium, potassium and sodium)* in the fluids inside and outside of cells after exercise, also requires energy and therefore oxygen.

Figure 2.4: *To show the relationship between oxygen deficit and EPOC*

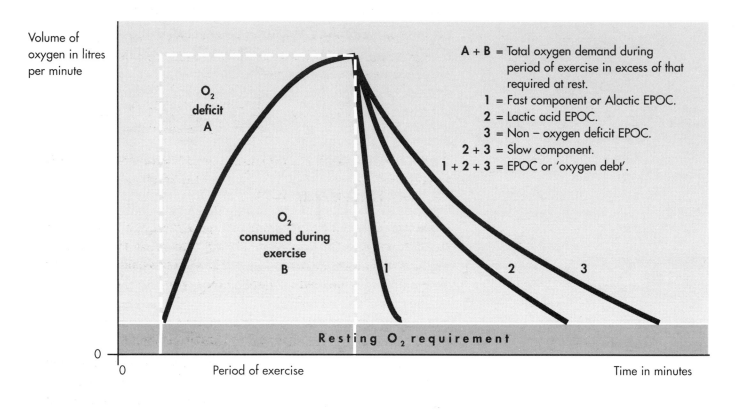

Volume of oxygen in litres per minute

O_2 deficit A

O_2 consumed during exercise B

A + B = Total oxygen demand during period of exercise in excess of that required at rest.
1 = Fast component or Alactic EPOC.
2 = Lactic acid EPOC.
3 = Non − oxygen deficit EPOC.
2 + 3 = Slow component.
1 + 2 + 3 = EPOC or 'oxygen debt'.

Resting O_2 requirement

0

Period of exercise   Time in minutes

2.7 ENERGY EFFICIENCY

The energy released by the oxidation of energy-rich substrates in respiration can be estimated indirectly from the net oxygen cost of a particular steady state activity. The **net oxygen cost** being the amount of oxygen used in the activity, above that which would have been consumed in an equivalent period of rest. For example the oxidation of 180 g glucose requires 134.4 dm^3 (litres) of oxygen, and releases 2867 kJ of energy.

Therefore, for a given volume of oxygen uptake the energy released can be calculated. However, the energy released for a given volume of oxygen varies, depending upon whether carbohydrates, fats, or proteins are oxidised.

Which particular substrate is used can be estimated from the **respiratory exchange ratio** *(RER)* or **respiratory quotient** *(RQ)*, where

$$RER = \frac{\text{Volume of } CO_2 \text{ output per minute}}{\text{Volume of } O_2 \text{ uptake per minute}} = \frac{\dot{V}_{CO_2}}{\dot{V}_{O_2}}$$

The values for carbohydrates, fats, and proteins are 1.0, 0.7, and 0.8 respectively. Intermediate figures result from the oxidation of mixtures of substrates, and any anaerobic respiration.

Having calculated the energy released from the net oxygen cost of a period of exercise, an attempt can be made to calculate the efficiency of the system, where :

$$\% \text{ Efficiency} = \frac{\text{Useful Work Output}}{\text{Energy Released}} \times 100$$

If the activity used in the measurement of useful work output is weight bearing, as on a treadmill, then the results should be calculated per unit body weight

There are inefficiencies in the trapping of energy in ATP, and in converting the chemical energy of ATP into useful mechanical work. So it is estimated that overall human movement is at best about 25% efficient with regard to energy use.

❖ *Training and Performance Applications*

Maximum efficiency occurs at a specific optimum work rate, above which there can be a dramatic fall off in efficiency. So that in endurance events, operating at the optimum rate can lead to large energy savings, and therefore to greater improvements in performance than could be achieved by greater effort. This is particularly well illustrated in cycling, where the correct riding position and use of gears is of the utmost importance.

2.7.1 GENERATION OF HEAT

The energy that is not trapped in ATP, and ultimately even the energy that is released from the ATP in doing work, is all lost as heat.

Therefore, the amount of energy released from the oxidation of respiratory substrates, is equal to the amount of heat given off by the body. As this occurs over the skin, the results should be calculated per unit surface area of the body.

The energy released as heat is not wasted, it enables the body to maintain a core body temperature of 37°C, which provides optimum conditions for the enzyme controlled activities of metabolism.

2.8 HEAT AND FLUID BALANCE DURING EXERCISE

If the body temperature rises above about 37°C, then the blood vessels in the dermis of the skin shunt more blood towards the surface, increasing the amount of heat lost by radiation, convection, and conduction to the surroundings, if the external temperature is lower than body temperature.

If the core body temperature rises to 0.5°C above normal, sweating begins. Energy is required to change the state of water from liquid to vapour, and this is known as the latent heat of evaporation. When sweat evaporates from the skin it absorbs this heat energy from the body, lowering the body temperature. One dm³ (litre) of sweat removes about 2424.4 kJ (579 Calories) of energy from the body. Under conditions of high relative humidity sweat may not evaporate, and if it accumulates on the skin it has no cooling effect.

❖ *Training and Performance Applications*

During exercise more heat is generated than at rest, and this speeds up the enzyme controlled processes involved in muscle contraction, which in turn aids exercise. This is one reason why a 'warm-up' period improves performance. However, if the body temperature rises above a certain critical limit, temperature control mechanisms come into operation. If these cannot cope, the body temperature may rise causing a drop in performance; if the temperature continues to rise above a certain critical level 'heat stroke' can occur which may be fatal.

2.8.1 WATER LOSS

During exercise there can be large water losses via sweating. The volume of water lost depends on the external temperature and humidity, the amount of exercise, and the volume of water drunk before and during exercise. Losses can vary from 1 - 3 dm³ (litres) per hour. This can lead to decreased plasma volume and consequent circulatory problems, such as decreased stroke volume and increased heart rate, there may also be reduced blood pressure and reduced tissue fluid formation. Also, even minor dehydration impairs muscle function. With more severe dehydration the increased concentration of salts in the plasma can interfere with normal heart function, leading to possible heart failure. In addition several hours of sweating can lead to sweat gland fatigue.

At high exercise intensities there can be competition for blood between the active muscles and the skin, and the flow to the skin can be reduced in favour of maintaining the blood flow to the active muscles. This will reduce the heat loss from the skin.

❖ *Training and Performance Applications*

Training increases the functional capacity and sensitivity of the sweating response, with sweating starting at a lower body temperature, and larger volumes of more dilute sweat being secreted, than in untrained subjects. If weight loss due to dehydration is greater than 2% of body weight after a particularly hard session, then further training should not be undertaken until the losses are made good. At a critical point of water loss during exercise sweating stops, to maintain the blood volume, and the core body temperature rises dramatically with heat stroke occurring at around 40.5°C. Fluid and energy losses are best replenished by drinking a cold (8-13°C) 2.5% solution of complex carbohydrates, such as maltodextrins from partially broken down starch. Such drinks empty from the stomach as fast as pure water, and go some way to replacing energy losses. Recommended amounts are, 500 cm³ 30 minutes before exercise commences, and 150 cm³ at 15 minute intervals during exercise, especially in events lasting longer than 60 minutes. The subjective sense of 'thirst' is not an accurate indicator of the amount of water needed, so drinks should be taken as a matter of course, rather than only when feeling thirsty.

Salts are also lost in the sweat, the most important being sodium chloride. Generally there is a lower sodium concentration in the sweat than in the plasma, therefore sweating does not decrease the plasma sodium concentration. However, if the fluid losses are replaced by drinking pure water, the plasma sodium level does decrease, and this is implicated in muscle cramps. Also as a result of this decrease in concentration of the fluids which surround the cells, water is drawn by osmosis into the cells, causing swelling of the tissues.

SUMMARY

❖ Glycerol, fatty acids, glucose, and amino acids can all be used as respiratory substrates, and have metabolic pathways in common.

❖ Fats are the main respiratory substrate in aerobic respiration. They cannot be broken down anaerobically. For a given volume of oxygen fats yield less ATP than carbohydrates.

❖ Carbohydrates become more important as an energy source as the intensity of exercise increases, because they are the only substrates that can be broken down anaerobically as well as aerobically. However,their supplies are limited.

❖ Proteins yield amino acids. Excess amino acids cannot be stored in the body, they are deaminated in the liver to produce urea, and the remainder of the molecule enters the respiratory pathway to be oxidised with the release of energy.

❖ The hormones adrenaline, noradrenaline and glucagon increase the availability of energy for exercise. Insulin decreases the availability of energy for exercise.

❖ There are three components of the energy supply system, alactic anaerobic, lactic anaerobic, and aerobic. All are involved in all exercise to varying degrees.

❖ The alactic anaerobic phosphagen system of ATP and PC represents the most immediately available source of energy for muscles, especially in powerful contractions. ATP can be resynthesised using energy from PC, anaerobic respiration and aerobic respiration. PC can only be resynthesised using energy from ATP.

❖ Anaerobic respiration generates little ATP, and results in the production of lactic acid, which contributes to fatigue and breathlessness.

❖ The point at which the intensity of exercise results in the accumulation of lactic acid in the blood is known as the 'anaerobic threshold' or Onset of Blood Lactate Accumulation *(OBLA)*.

❖ Aerobic respiration generates much more ATP, and results in the complete oxidation of respiratory substrates, for example glucose, to carbon dioxide and water.

❖ Thresholds occur when one energy supply system is displaced as the major energy supply system by another.

❖ The amount of oxygen one is short of during exercise *(thus causing anaerobic respiration to occur)* is known as the oxygen deficit.

❖ The concept of oxygen 'debt' is not simply involved with the 'repayment' of an oxygen deficit incurred during exercise. Therefore a better term is the 'excess post exercise oxygen consumption' *(EPOC)*.

❖ The efficiency of energy usage can be calculated from the net oxygen cost of a particular activity and the useful work output. With maximum efficiency occurring at an optimum work rate.

❖ The substrate being used in respiration can be estimated from the respiratory exchange ratio *(RER)* or respiratory quotient *(RQ)*.

❖ All energy is ultimately lost as heat over the surface of the skin.

❖ Heat loss is by convection, conduction, radiation and sweating. At high exercise intensities blood is withdrawn from the skin as it is shunted to the working muscles, thus reducing heat loss.

❖ Sweating results in water and salt loss, which can have a critical effect on the efficiency of exercise.

CIRCULATION IN ACTION

OBJECTIVES

To enable the reader to understand the following.

❖ The structure and function of the heart.

❖ The cardiac output as a product of the heart rate and stroke volume.

❖ The ways in which the heart adapts to exercise in both the short and long term.

❖ Blood pressure and its regulation with respect to exercise.

❖ The role of blood vessels in the circulation of the blood during exercise.

❖ The formation of tissue fluid and the role of the lymphatic system.

3.1 THE STRUCTURE OF THE HEART

The heart is a four chambered muscular pump which contracts rhythmically to force the blood around the body. One-way valves ensure that the blood flows through the heart in the correct direction

Figure 3.1: *The Human heart - internal structure. Note that deoxygenated blood from the body flows from the venae cavae into the right atrium, into the right ventricle, and to the lungs in the pulmonary arteries. Oxygenated blood returns from the lungs in the pulmonary veins into the left atrium, into the left ventricle, and to the body in the main aorta.*

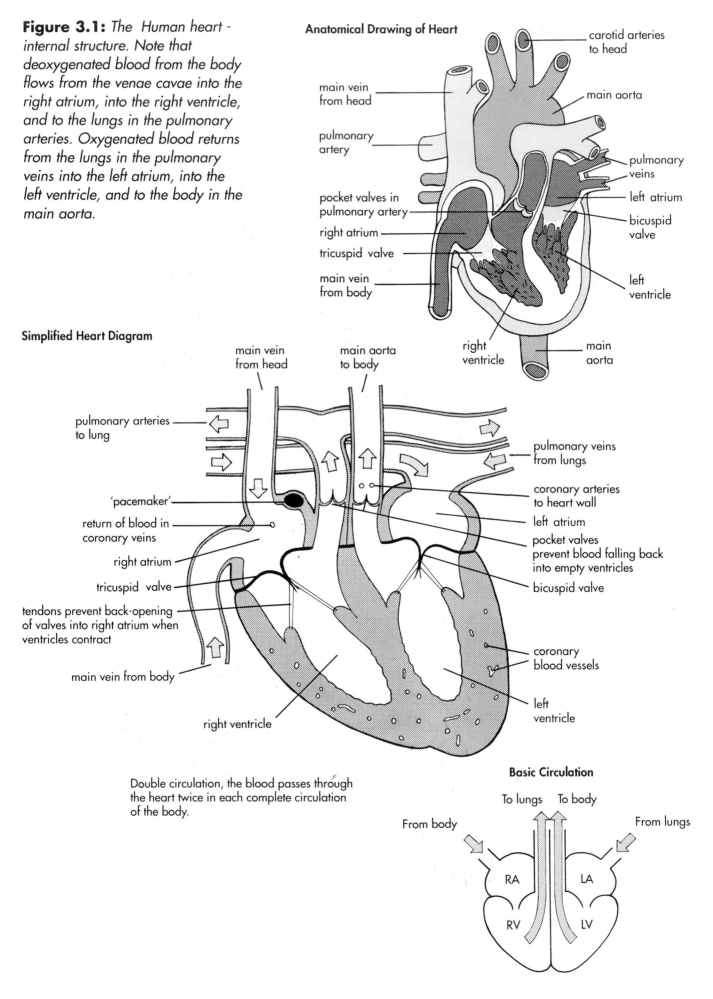

Anatomical Drawing of Heart

carotid arteries to head

main vein from head

main aorta

pulmonary artery

pulmonary veins

pocket valves in pulmonary artery

left atrium

right atrium

bicuspid valve

tricuspid valve

main vein from body

left ventricle

right ventricle

main aorta

Simplified Heart Diagram

main vein from head

main aorta to body

pulmonary arteries to lung

pulmonary veins from lungs

'pacemaker'

coronary arteries to heart wall

return of blood in coronary veins

left atrium

right atrium

pocket valves prevent blood falling back into empty ventricles

tricuspid valve

bicuspid valve

tendons prevent back-opening of valves into right atrium when ventricles contract

coronary blood vessels

main vein from body

left ventricle

right ventricle

Double circulation, the blood passes through the heart twice in each complete circulation of the body.

Basic Circulation

To lungs   To body

From body

From lungs

RA   LA

RV   LV

Figure 3.2: *Diagrammatic representation of the human circulation system.*

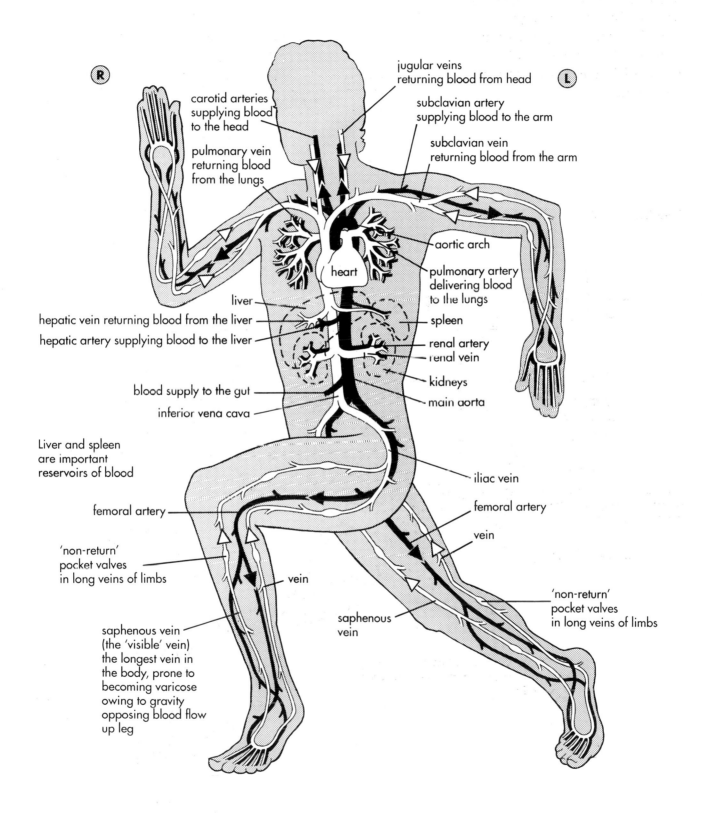

Figure 3.3: *The cardiac cycle.*

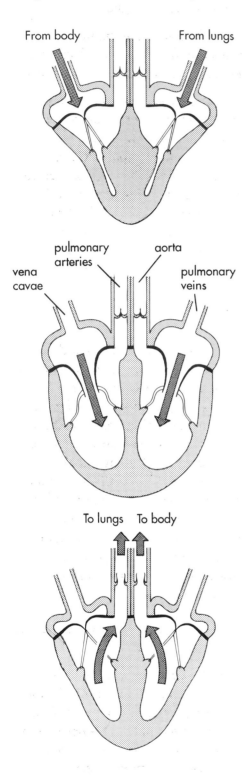

3.2 THE FUNCTION OF THE HEART

3.2.1 CARDIAC CYCLE

The sequence of events that occurs during the filling and emptying of the heart is known as the cardiac cycle.

At a rate of 70 beats per minute (bpm) the complete cycle takes about 0.86 seconds. It is a continuous sequence of events, but for the purposes of explanation it is convenient to consider it as occurring in a series of stages

There is a point in the cardiac cycle when all the heart valves are shut, which can be taken as the starting point.

Blood returning under low pressure in the main veins *(superior and inferior venae cavae)* from the upper and lower body enters the right atrium, and at the same time blood returning from the lungs in the pulmonary veins enters the left atrium.

The atria fill with blood, and the rising pressure of the blood in the atria pushes the tricuspid and bicuspid valves open, and both ventricles begin to fill. As the heart fills with blood both atria contract *(atrial systole)* forcing even more blood into the ventricles. These are now stretched, and they both contract *(ventricular systole)* forcing the blood upwards. This upsurge of blood forces the tricuspid and bicuspid valves shut. These valves are prevented from back-opening into the atria by tough cords, which are held taut by contraction of the papillary muscles to which they are attached. The closing of these valves makes the first heart sound.

The blood is thus forced along the pulmonary artery to the lungs, and along the main aorta to the rest of the body, forcing open both sets of pocket or semi-lunar valves on the way.

When the ventricles relax *(ventricular diastole)* the blood tends to fall back down the pulmonary artery and main aorta under gravity, thus filling and shutting the pocket valves. The closing of these valves makes the second heart sound. All valves are now shut and the cycle is repeated.

3.2.2 CARDIAC MUSCLE

The muscle tissue of the heart wall is a special type known as cardiac muscle. Cardiac muscle is composed of short striated fibres interconnected by side branches, which allow for the rapid spread of excitation from fibre to fibre throughout the heart wall.

Cardiac muscle has a long refractory or rest period *(during which it cannot be restimulated)*, so that no merging or summation can occur between successive contractions. This ensures that the heart as a whole beats in a rhythmic fashion, with a period of rest or diastole between contractions, during which it can refill. The rest period also protects the cardiac muscle from fatigue.

Cardiac muscle cannot respire anaerobically to any significant extent, and being aerobic it uses glucose, fatty acids and lactic acid *(formed in the exercising muscles)* as respiratory substrates or fuels.

Of all tissues, cardiac muscle has the highest concentration of mitochondria *(organelles within cells which are the centres of aerobic respiration)*, and each fibre is supplied with at least one capillary. Therefore cardiac muscle has a high capability for aerobic respiration *(oxidative potential)*, being able to extract up to 80% of the oxygen from the blood even at rest *(compared to as little as 25% extraction by other tissues)*. As a result of this high extraction of oxygen at rest, the increased demand for oxygen during exercise can only be supplied by an increase in coronary blood flow.

3.2.3 CORONARY BLOOD SUPPLY

The cardiac muscle of the heart wall is supplied with blood via the coronary arteries. These arise from the main aorta, just above the pocket valves. In this position their supply of blood is continuous, irrespective of the state of contraction of the heart. There is less flow in the coronary arteries during systole as they are compressed by the contraction of the cardiac muscle. As the heart rate increases during exercise, diastole shortens more than systole. This would be expected to reduce the diastolic coronary blood flow. However, there is still an increase in coronary flow from about 250 cm^3 per minute at rest to 1000 cm^3 per minute during exercise, as a result of increased dilation of the coronary blood vessels which is stimulated by hypoxia *(a drop in the oxygen level in the cardiac muscle)*, and by increased aortic pressure which forces more blood into the vessels.

❖ *Training and Performance Applications*

Aerobic training increases the stroke volume, and therefore also lowers the resting heart rate, thus increasing the period of diastole in each cardiac cycle, and allowing greater coronary blood flow. A low heart rate and a high stroke volume is the most efficient way of achieving a given cardiac output, and as a result of this, the cardiac muscle of the trained heart needs less oxygen and therefore a proportionally lower coronary blood supply at rest than the untrained heart.

As a result of the special properties of cardiac muscle, the heart cannot develop an oxygen debt to any significant extent, nor can it develop 'cramp', as can occur in other muscle tissue.

It is generally agreed that a healthy heart cannot be damaged or 'strained' by exercise, no matter how strenuous. However if cardiac

It is important to remember that the heart responds to the **demands** of the body, especially the skeletal muscles, whose demand for oxygen can increase up to twenty times during exercise. The heart is therefore responding to feedback information from the tissues. In this way the cardiac output is adjusted to maintain the necessary blood supply under the correct pressure to the tissues.

A greater cardiac output requires an equivalent increase in the return of blood to the heart. This venous return of blood to the heart is affected by the position of the body. For example during upright exercise such as running there are difficulties in increasing venous return against the force of gravity, so the central blood volume is decreased, reducing the venous return and the stroke volume, and resulting in an increase of the heart rate for a given cardiac output. In the horizontal position venous return is not opposed by gravity, and therefore during exercise, such as swimming, there are less problems in ensuring adequate venous return, the central blood volume and venous return are not decreased, therefore compared to the situation in running the stroke volume is greater and the heart rate slower for a given cardiac output.

3.3 ATHLETE'S HEART

The adaptations that the heart shows to aerobic exercise over a period of time, lead to the condition known as 'athlete's heart'.

There is enlargement *(hypertrophy)* of the heart giving an increased stroke volume and a reduced resting heart rate, which is often irregular and associated with abnormal electrical activity *(ECG)*. This abnormal activity can result in misdiagnoses if the examining physician is unaware of the training background.

There is increased capillarisation of the cardiac muscle, but it is not clear whether this is due to the development of new capillaries, or the more complete use of existing ones.

The individual myofibrils in the cardiac muscle fibres thicken and increase in number, and there is an increase in the size and number of the mitochondria.

The healthy untrained heart does not experience insufficient oxygen supply *(hypoxia)* even during maximum exercise, but the adaptations seen in 'athletes heart' are an advantage, as they enable the heart to function at a lower percentage of its total oxidative capacity during exercise.

❖ *Training and Performance Applications*

Training induced changes of the heart may be considered as either **functional**, *or* **structural**. *Functional changes, such as an increase in contractility of the cardiac muscle, are rapid and occur within weeks; but structural changes, such as the enlargement of the ventricles takes months or even years. These changes are reversed over a period of time once the training load is decreased, which is a contributory cause of the general reversibility of the training effect, as a result of which the level of performance returns to the pre-training level.*

3.4 BLOOD PRESSURE

The heart pumps blood around a complete circuit of vessels, which offer resistance to the flow of blood, therefore pressures are generated within the system. In a healthy adult, the pressure in the arteries close to the heart is highest *(120 millimetres (mm) of mercury (Hg))* when the ventricles are contracting, which is known as the **systolic blood pressure**, and lowest *(80 mm Hg)* when the ventricles are relaxing, which is known as the **diastolic blood pressure**.

The average of the systolic and diastolic pressures during a complete cardiac cycle, known as the **mean blood pressure**, determines the overall rate of blood flow through the circulation.

The blood pressure drops as the blood gets further away from the left ventricle and circulates around the body. Some typical figures for the mean blood pressure *(in mm Hg)* whilst at rest are: arteries 100, arterioles 60, capillaries 18, veins 7, and at the entrance to the right atrium 3.

Blood pressure is determined by the **cardiac output** and **the resistance to flow of the blood.** The resistance is often referred to as the peripheral resistance, as the major part of it occurs in the smaller vessels *(mainly the arterioles)* at a distance from the heart. The resistance to flow is due to the friction between the blood and the walls of the blood vessels. The friction is determined by the length, diameter, and the smoothness of the lining of the vessel; and the viscosity of the blood.

Arteries and arterioles *(and to a lesser extent veins and venules)* have involuntary muscle fibres in their walls, which when contracted constrict the vessel reducing its diameter. Also the diameter of the vessel is effectively reduced by any loss of elasticity of the vessel walls, such as occurs with age and/or the formation of fatty deposits *(plaques)* of cholesterol. The plaques also roughen the lining of the vessels which further increases the friction between the blood and the walls.

If the blood pressure begins to drop, there is an increased activity of the sympathetic nervous system. This increases the heart rate and stroke volume, and therefore the cardiac output. It also causes constriction of the arterioles and the veins, which increases the peripheral resistance. These changes result in a raising of the blood pressure back to normal. At the same time there is an an increase in the release of the hormones adrenaline and noradrenaline.

Adrenaline causes constriction of the arterioles *(vasoconstriction)* in the skin and the gut, but dilation of the vessels in the skeletal muscles, the liver, and the coronary circulation of the heart. It also increases the heart rate and cardiac output. Thus also contributing to the rise in blood pressure.

Noradrenaline causes a net vasoconstriction overall, even in the skeletal muscles. As a result noradrenaline has a stronger effect in raising blood pressure than adrenaline.

In addition, the adrenal glands secrete the hormone aldosterone, which causes the kidneys to retain salts and water. This increases the blood volume and therefore the blood pressure.

If the blood pressure begins to rise, there is a reflex increase in the parasympathetic nerve impulses, which causes the heart rate to slow, decreasing the cardiac output. The blood vessels are also dilated which lowers the peripheral resistance, thus further reducing the blood pressure.

During exercise, although initially both the cardiac output and blood pressure increase, these various homeostatic mechanisms act to restrict the rise in blood pressure, and to eventually bring it down.

3.5 ROLE OF VESSELS IN THE CIRCULATION OF THE BLOOD

The blood circulates around a continuous system of blood vessels, the arteries, arterioles, capillaries, venules and veins.

3.5.1 ARTERIES

The arteries close to the heart have a large cross sectional area, and thick elastic walls. The large elastic arteries are stretched by the cardiac output of ventricular systole, and they recoil when the arterial blood pressure drops during ventricular diastole. This recoil assists the circulation of the blood around the body, helps smooth the flow between contractions of the heart, and helps to maintain the blood pressure. This stretching and recoiling of the arteries is felt as **the pulse.**

3.5.2 ARTERIOLES

Further from the heart, the arteries branch into the smaller arterioles. The arterioles penetrate all tissues of the body and connect to beds of finely branching capillaries. There are so many capillaries in the body, that they cannot all be supplied with blood at the same time. Therefore there is competition for blood between different regions of the body, especially during exercise, when blood must be **shunted** to the working muscles, and consequently withdrawn from other regions. For example, when the body is at rest, about 45% of the cardiac output passes through the capillaries of the gut wall and associated glands, and the kidneys. During maximum exercise this can be reduced to about 3% of the cardiac output, as blood is redirected to the working muscles. This does not necessarily lead to as large a reduction in oxygen supply to the gut and kidneys as it would seem, as these regions only use about 10 - 25% of the oxygen available in their normal blood supply. The reduced flow rate is therefore compensated for by a greater extraction of oxygen from the blood, by these tissues. However, prolonged reduction in the blood flow to the gut and its associated glands will inevitably interfere with digestion. In short intense periods of exercise the blood flow to the skin is also reduced, even in hot conditions, as it is shunted to the muscles. However, it is increased in longer duration moderate exercise in order to promote heat loss as part of temperature control.

The shunting of blood between competing tissues is achieved by constriction and dilation of the arterioles, and of the arterio-venous vessels, which are direct connections between the arterioles and venules, from which the capillary beds arise. The entrances to the capillary beds are controlled by circular pre-capillary sphincter muscles, which when contracted shut off the capillaries, and when relaxed open them.

Table 3.1: *Estimated blood flow in cm³ per minute, to different organs/systems in a trained male at rest and during maximum effort.*

Estimated blood flow in cm³ per minute

Organ system	At rest	%	Max. effort*	%
Skeletal muscle	1000	20	26 000	88.00
Coronary vessels	250	5	1200	4.00
Skin	500	10	750	2.50
Kidneys	1000	20	300	1.00
Liver & gut	1250	25	375	1.25
Brain	750	15	750	2.50
Whole body	5000	100	30 000	100.00

*Cycle ergometer

❖ *Training and Performance Application*

As the withdrawal of blood from the gut to supply active muscles inevitably interferes with digestion, vigorous exercise should not be undertaken until at least three hours after eating a meal. Very long distance endurance performances require some form of energy intake during the event, as is seen in cycle racing, long distance swimming and ultra distance running, but measures are taken to keep the 'digestion load' to a minimum by taking in readily digestible and absorbable food. The reduction of blood flow to the liver and kidneys during exercise may be a contributory factor to fatigue, as these organs are involved in the removal of waste products produced during exercise. The removal of blood from the liver can cause the liver to shrink, stimulating pain receptors in the covering membranes, which is one explanation of the 'stitch'. Another explanation of the 'stitch' is that it is caused as a result of cramp or spasm of various muscles in the chest and/or abdomen, such as the diaphragm, between the ribs, or in the stomach wall. Alternatively it is suggested that stretching of the membranes holding the abdominal organs in place, especially when running where there is a 'bouncing action' could be the cause. This last explanation is supported by the observation that the 'stitch' is relatively rare amongst cyclists and swimmers with their smoother non-jarring action, and that 70% of all stitches occur on the right hand side where the liver, the heaviest organ in the abdominal cavity is suspended beneath the diaphragm. It is suggested that by breathing out when the left foot hits the ground, and breathing in when the right foot hits the ground, the diaphragm will be moving down with the liver at the point of right foot impact, thus lessening the risk and/or effects of a stitch.

3.5.3 CONTROL OF BLOOD SHUNTING

All the arterioles, and the precapillary sphincters which control the entrance of blood into the capillary networks, are supplied with vasoconstrictor nerves from the sympathetic nervous system.

Stimulation by impulses from these nerves causes vasoconstriction (a narrowing of the diameter) of the arterioles, and contraction of the precapillary sphincters which closes off the capillary beds, reducing the blood flow to the regions that they supply.

In addition, the adrenal glands secrete adrenaline and noradrenaline which cause the effects described earlier *(Section 3.4.1, p 69)*. However, during exercise this hormonal influence is less important than the faster sympathetic control.

The blood vessels supplying the cardiac muscle of the heart, and the skeletal muscles, are also supplied with sympathetic vasodilator nerves, which cause the muscle in the walls of the vessels to relax and the vessels to dilate, increasing the blood supply to the regions they supply. However, the major influences on vasodilation in the muscles are the local factors generated in the exercising muscles themselves. These local factors within the working muscle include a drop in the oxygen, and a rise in the carbon dioxide levels; a decrease in pH *(increase in acidity)*; an increase in temperature; an increase in the amount of ADP present in the muscle fibres; and an increase in potassium and magnesium ions in the muscles. These factors act directly on the involuntary muscle of the small arterioles, arterio-venous vessels, and precapillary sphincters, causing vasodilation. This effect is virtually instantaneous, and being controlled by products of muscle activity, is finely attuned to supplying the exact requirements of the working muscles. These local factors also stimulate highly sensitive sensory nerve endings which trigger the sympathetic vasodilation reflexes.

3.5.4 CAPILLARIES

The capillaries form a fine network which penetrate all tissues. They have the smallest diameter of all blood vessels, about 7 micrometres *(0.007 mm)*, which is the same as that of the red blood corpuscles. Therefore the corpuscles are forced to move slowly through the capillaries in single file, allowing the corpuscles to come close to the surrounding tissues, ensuring a short diffusion distance between them. Capillary walls are just one cell thick, which further aids exchanges by diffusion between the blood and the tissues. Also the huge number of capillaries provide a very large surface area across which these exchanges occur. As more capillaries open up in the working muscles, the surface area between the blood and tissues is increased, and the diffusion distance between the two is decreased, resulting in more rapid and efficient exchanges between them. For example total oxygen uptake by the muscles can increase up to twenty times during exercise.

3.5.5 TISSUE FLUID

As a result of the positive pressure of the blood, plasma is forced out through the walls of the capillaries to form tissue fluid. This tissue fluid carries oxygen, nutrients, hormones and antibodies, from the capillaries out into direct contact with the cells of the

Figure 4.1: *The Human thorax and lungs.*

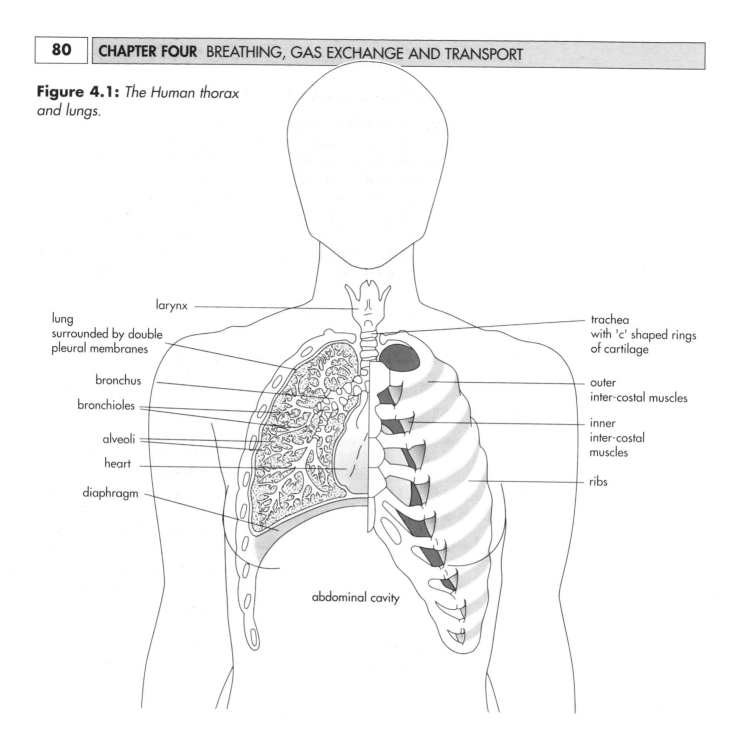

larynx

lung
surrounded by double
pleural membranes

bronchus

bronchioles

alveoli

heart

diaphragm

trachea
with 'c' shaped rings
of cartilage

outer
inter-costal muscles

inner
inter-costal
muscles

ribs

abdominal cavity

4.2 BREATHING MOVEMENTS

4.2.1 INSPIRATION or BREATHING IN

Inspiration is an active process. The external intercostal muscles contract, causing the ribs and sternum to move upwards and outwards. At the same time, the diaphragm muscles contract, causing the central part of the diaphragm to move down, so that the diaphragm flattens. These movements of the ribs, sternum, and diaphragm cause the thorax and the lungs to increase in volume, and the air pressure within the lungs to decrease below the external air pressure. As a result the external air pressure forces air from the outside into the lungs.

Figure 4.2: *Side view of thorax to show breathing movements.*

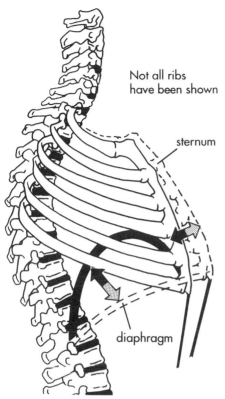

Not all ribs have been shown

sternum

diaphragm

Muscles relaxed

Volume of thorax decreases, pressure increases, air forced out.

Ribs swing down and in.

Diaphragm returns to relaxed position.

Muscles contracted

Volume of thorax increases, pressure decreases, external air pressure forces air in.

Ribs swing up and out.

Diaphragm contracts and flattens.

4.2.2 EXPIRATION or BREATHING OUT

In normal quiet breathing, expiration is passive. The external intercostal muscles relax, and the ribs and sternum move downwards and inwards regaining their original positions. At the same time, the diaphragm muscles relax, and the central part of the diaphragm moves up, so that the diaphragm regains its domed shape. These movements of the ribs, sternum, and diaphragm, aided by the elastic recoil of the thoracic tissues and abdominal muscles, cause the thorax and the lungs to decrease in volume, and the air pressure within the lungs to increase above the external air pressure. As a result the greater internal pressure forces air out of the lungs.

In forced breathing, for example during exercise, expiration is active. The internal intercostal muscles contract, moving the ribs and sternum downwards more forcibly. The abdominal muscles also contract, increasing the pressure in the abdominal cavity, which helps to force the central part of the diaphragm up.

❖ *Training and Performance Applications*

The strength and efficiency of the respiratory muscles are increased as a result of the work they perform in strenuous exercise. Although this is a contributory factor to the 'easing' of breathing difficulties that is seen with increasing fitness, rather surprisingly it is not the major one (the major one being the increasing efficiency of the circulatory system). In heavy exercise the muscles involved in breathing movements can themselves utilise up to 10% of the oxygen uptake. Cramp of these muscles may be one cause of the 'stitch', but this is far from certain in all cases.

4.2.3 CONTROL OF BREATHING MOVEMENTS

Breathing movements are under nervous control, which in turn is influenced by chemical and mechanical changes associated with exercise.

Normal breathing movements are controlled by involuntary, automatic, rhythmic discharges of nerve impulses from the regions of the brain known as the **respiratory control centres.**

The **inspiratory control centre** sends motor nerve impulses to the external intercostal muscles of the ribs, and the muscles of the diaphragm, causing them to contract, and inspiration to occur. This active phase of the inspiratory control centre lasts for about two seconds. After this it automatically stops sending motor impulses for about three seconds, during which time the muscles of inspiration relax and expiration follows passively.

The basic rhythm of nervous control by the respiratory control centres is influenced by sensory inputs so that breathing alters in response to the demands of the body during exercise.

During forced breathing, when the inspiratory control centre reaches the end of each of its periods of rhythmic discharge, it sends nerve impulses to activate the **expiratory control centre**. Motor impulses from here stimulate the internal intercostal muscles and abdominal muscles to contract, resulting in forced expiration.

Ventilation of the lungs is a function of the **rate** and **depth** of breathing. Early on in exercise, ventilation is mainly increased by an increase in the depth of breathing, whilst later it is the rate of breathing that increases more.

Any increase in the acidity of the blood *(decrease in blood pH)* causes an increase in ventilation. A decrease in pH results mainly from an increase in the production of lactic acid and carbon dioxide *(an 'acid' gas)*, due to the increase in the rate of respiration associated with exercise. The level of acidity is monitored by chemoreceptors in the main aorta and in the carotid bodies in the arteries of the neck. Indeed, the sensitivity of the carotid bodies to a decrease in pH is thought to be a major factor controlling the increase in ventilation rate, during exercise, along with nervous stimulation of the respiratory control centres from the contracting muscles and moving joints.

The respiratory control centres have connections with the cerebral cortex, so that a degree of voluntary control can be exerted over breathing movements, which is necessary for speech. However, once the pH decreases below, and the carbon dioxide in the blood rises above, a certain level, the inspiratory control centre is stimulated, and voluntary control is over-ridden. It is these factors rather than shortage of oxygen that limit breath holding activities.

The blood has a certain buffering capacity, ie under normal conditions it can resist changes in its pH *(acidity or alkalinity)*, restricting the changes in blood pH to between 7.2 and 7.45. As the lactic acid accumulates in the blood, it is buffered *(initially at least)* by combination with the hydrogen carbonate ions present in the plasma, increasing the amount of carbon dioxide in the blood.

$$H^+ \text{(from lactic acid)} + HCO_3^- \longrightarrow H_2CO_3 \longrightarrow H_2O + CO_2$$

An increase in the level of CO_2 in the blood stimulates the chemoreceptors in the carotid bodies, but its main effect is by direct stimulation of the respiratory control centres in the brain, resulting in an increase in the ventilation rate, and therefore more CO_2 being exhaled by the lungs.

Past a certain point the buffering capacity of the blood *(due also to the plasma proteins and the haemoglobin in the red blood corpuscles)* is saturated, and in strenuous exercise the pH within the muscles can drop to 6.4, and the arterial blood pH to about 7.0 or just below, as a result of the accumulation of lactic acid. Typically the ventilation of the lungs during exercise increases in proportion to the increase in heart rate and to the uptake of oxygen, however as the level of lactic acid reaches 4 millimoles per dm^3 (litre) of blood the rate of ventilation of the lungs increases more rapidly than the heart rate and the oxygen uptake. This point, at which ventilation 'breaks away' from the heart rate and oxygen uptake, is known as the **'ventilation break point'**. Past this point, although the rate of ventilation increases, there is no further increase in the uptake of oxygen. This point is also known as the 'anaerobic threshold' or OBLA *(Section 2.5.2, p48)*.

❖ *Training and Performance Applications*

In terms of aerobic endurance the greater the aerobic capacity and the greater the percentage of the aerobic capacity at which OBLA occurs, the better will be the performance. However the exercise intensity just above the OBLA is of greater significance to the performance than the aerobic capacity itself. For example if there were two endurance athletes with equal aerobic capacities, the one who could use the largest percentage of that aerobic capacity without accumulating lactic acid would have the better performance, all other things being equal. In fact some World ranked endurance athletes have had a relatively low aerobic capacity. Both can be improved by training, but the greatest gains can be made in the percentage aerobic capacity at which OBLA occurs. Thus highly trained athletes can perform for long periods at up to 80% of their aerobic capacity before OBLA and exhaustion occur.

The chemoreceptors in the carotid bodies and the aorta are also sensitive to levels of oxygen in the blood, although less so than to levels of pH and carbon dioxide. A decrease in the level of oxygen stimulates an increase in ventilation.

Stretch receptors in the bronchi and the bronchioles are stimulated by the expansion of the lungs. Nerve impulses pass from these along sensory nerves to the inspiratory control centre, causing the reflex inhibition of the inspiratory motor nerve impulses. Therefore the muscles of inspiration relax, and expiration follows passively. However, this mechanism is not thought to be part of the normal control of breathing, but operates to protect the lungs from over-inflation.

Other sensory receptors *(proprioceptors)* in the skeleton and muscles, also feedback sensory information to increase breathing movements during exercise.

In conclusion it should be noted that the changes in blood levels of carbon dioxide, pH, and oxygen, together with mechanical feedback, cannot fully account for the large and rapid changes in ventilation

Figure 4.3: *Spirometer trace.*

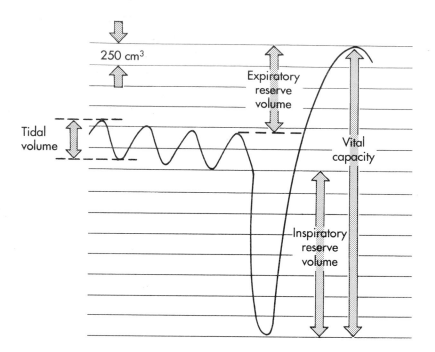

The volume of air breathed-in, in one minute, is known as the **Minute Volume**. That is the tidal volume multiplied by the breathing rate per minute. During quiet breathing this can be:

$$500 \text{ cm}^3 \times 16 = 8000 \text{ cm}^3 \ (8.0 \text{ dm}^3)$$

The tidal volume increases from about 12% of the vital capacity at rest, to about 50-60% of the vital capacity during exercise, and the breathing rate can increase to up to 50 per minute. Therefore the minute volume in a normally fit male can rise to:

$$3000 \text{ cm}^3 \times 50 = 150\ 000 \text{ cm}^3$$

The **Maximum Voluntary Ventilation** *(MVV)* is the volume of air that can be breathed in 15 seconds of forced rapid and deep breathing, multiplied by 4, to give a figure for one minute. In males this can typically be up to 200 000 cm³ per minute, which is a greater volume than can be breathed during maximum exercise.

The **Timed Vital Capacity** or **Forced Expiratory Volume** (FEV_1) is that percentage of the vital capacity *(normally about 85%)* that can be expired in one second. This gives a measure of the overall resistance to air flow which is an important factor in the ventilation of the lungs.

Resistance to air flow in the air tubes accounts for up to 80% of the total resistance of the lungs to ventilation, particularly during expiration when the airways tend to collapse. The remainder of the resistance is due to the elasticity or **compliance** of the lung tissues.

❖ *Training and Performance Applications*

During exercise, adrenaline and an increase in sympathetic nervous activity, cause the smooth muscle fibres in the walls of the airways to relax, resulting in dilation of the airways and a decrease in the resistance to air flow. For this reason restrictions exist over the use of asthmatic inhalers by competitors, as they work on the principle of dilating the airways. In cold air, the airways and pulmonary capillaries constrict, decreasing the efficiency of ventilation and gas exchange.

4.4 GAS EXCHANGE AT THE LUNGS

Gas exchange occurs between the air in the alveoli of the lungs and the blood in the capillaries present in the walls of the alveoli of the lungs.

4.4.1 DIFFUSION

A substance, as a gas or in solution, will move by diffusion from a region of its higher concentration to a region of its lower concentration, down a concentration gradient, until an equilibrium is reached. An increase in temperature increases the speed of diffusion. An increase in the differences of concentration between two regions, that is an increase in the concentration gradient, increases the amount of substance diffusing, but not its speed of diffusion.

4.4.2 PARTIAL PRESSURE

The continuous random movement of particles of a gas means that the particles will occasionally collide with each other and with the walls of any structure enclosing them within a space, thus exerting a pressure. The number of such collisions, and therefore the pressure, is proportional to the amount of substance present. In mixtures of gases, e.g. air, each substance exerts a partial pressure in that mixture proportional to the amount of that substance in the mixture.

The partial pressure of a gas is a better measure of the amount of gas present than quoting its concentration as a percentage *(e.g. 21% oxygen in air)*, because, for example, although the *percentage* of oxygen remains the same in air under different conditions, the *amount* of oxygen does not. At atmospheric pressures less than at sea level e.g. at altitude, there is still 21% oxygen in air, but as the air is less dense there is a smaller amount of oxygen.

disease. Several are not related to exercise and are not dealt with here, e.g. inherited disposition, personality 'type' *(also with an inherited element)*, stress, diet, smoking, and some forms of oral contraceptives in females. Others are related to exercise, such as obesity, hypertension *(high blood pressure)*, high blood cholesterol, and diabetes or high blood glucose.

Obesity is inter-related with other risk factors including hypertension and high blood cholesterol, but just being overweight in itself carries an increased risk of heart disease. In association with a properly balanced diet, aerobic exercise can reduce obesity and help maintain an ideal body weight, for example cycling for one hour can use about 600 Calories (2520 kJ), and jogging for one hour can use about 1000 Calories *(4200 kJ)* - the equivalent of about 5 ounces (142 g) of body fat. A reduction in obesity also relieves stress on joints, increases flexibility, and can have psychological benefits.

Hypertension or high blood pressure can be related to stress, smoking, obesity, or be of unknown cause, gradually increasing with age. Hypertensive subjects have a greater risk of cardio-vascular disease and strokes. Aerobic exercise dilates the arterioles supplying the large muscle masses of the body, and by thus decreasing the peripheral resistance, decreases the blood pressure.

High blood cholesterol, or more accurately a high ratio of total blood cholesterol to high density lipoprotein *(HDL)* cholesterol, is associated with an increase in fatty deposits or plaques in the walls of blood vessels and the risk of coronary heart disease. Aerobic exercise decreases this ratio and therefore the risk, but whether aerobic exercise can actually reduce the fatty plaques once they are formed is not clear.

Due to poor diet and inactivity, these cardio-vascular disease risk factors of high blood pressure and high blood cholesterol ratios are increasingly being seen in childhood.

High blood glucose, as found in diabetes, is related to an increase in risk of cardio-vascular disease, which is the major cause of death in diabetics. Aerobic exercise, by maintaining the sensitivity of the tissues to insulin, plays a part in the prevention and/or capacity to cope with Type II *(mature onset non-insulin dependent)* diabetes, which is caused by a decrease in the sensitivity of the tissues to insulin, and not a deficiency of insulin.

Aerobic exercise increases the blood flow through the coronary arteries supplying the cardiac muscle of the heart wall, thus lowering the risk of a blood clot forming in these vessels *(coronary thrombosis)* and blocking the flow of blood and therefore the supply of oxygen and nutrients to the muscle fibres, which in the case of cardiac muscle cannot respire anaerobically. The risk of thrombosis is further reduced as a result of aerobic exercise increasing the rate at which any clots present are destroyed *(fibrinolysis)*, and inhibiting the aggregation of blood platelets which are involved in the formation of blood clots.

The effect of long term aerobic exercise in lowering the heart rate during sub-maximal exercise and at rest, reduces the demands on the heart. It also improves the stability of the electrical activity of the heart, which decreases the risk of life threatening disturbances in their pattern *(as seen in the ECG trace)*.

In summary, vigorous aerobic exercise at least three times a week reduces the risk of a 'heart attack' by at least 50%.

Exercise of all types has a beneficial effect on the musculo-skeletal system.

Muscles, tendons, ligaments and bones all weaken as a result of disuse. During prolonged inactivity up to a third of the calcium salts which are responsible for the hardness of bone can be lost in a process of demineralisation, leading to the weakening of the bone known as osteoporosis. Exercise protects against this bone loss, and can even more than compensate for the loss of bone mass that occurs past the age of about 40, and in post-menopausal osteoporosis in females. Exercise can also increase the tensile strength of tendons and ligaments, and as a result of the release of growth hormone stimulates the synthesis of tissue protein, especially in the muscles.

Exercise also helps in the management and control of various lung conditions, such as chronic bronchitis, asthma and emphysema.

By improving the quality of sleep, and aiding relaxation, exercise has a role in the control of stress, which in turn is risk factor in heart disease.

However, all these beneficial effects of exercise are reversible, and only persist if vigorous exercise is maintained.

SUMMARY

❖ Fitness and health are not simply defined, it is possible to be fit but unhealthy, and healthy but unfit. Fitness is frequently defined on the outcome of various 'fitness measures' which are neither valid *(ie they do not measure what it is claimed that they are measuring)* nor reliable *(ie they do not provide consistent results)*.

❖ Physical fitness has many different components, with some particularly relevant to health as well as to sport performance.

❖ There are many structural and functional *(physiological)* differences between males and females relevant to differences in sport performance; arising mainly from the higher levels of the male sex hormone testosterone in males.

❖ Children up to the age of puberty should be given special consideration with regard to training, based on a knowledge of their pattern of growth and development, both physical and mental.

❖ In the absence of any reason to the contrary, exercise is considered to be beneficial at all ages, with activity opposing many of the changes associated with ageing.

❖ Regular, carefully graded, aerobic exercise is generally considered beneficial to health; however, over exertion with inadequate recovery can lead to chronic *(long lasting)* ill health, especially in young adults.

TRAINING PRINCIPLES

OBJECTIVES

To enable the reader to understand the following.

❖ Training principles applicable to most sports.

❖ Continuous or steady state training regimes and their use.

❖ The use and limitations of training 'formulae' - Karvonen and Conconi

❖ Intermittent training regimes and their use; interval training, strength training, circuit training, stage training, skill training, and mobility training.

6.1 INTRODUCTION

The main principles of training, especially for strength and endurance, are specificity, isolation, progressive overload, recovery, reversibility; along with considerations of intensity, duration and frequency.

Training effects are very **specific** to the system being particularly stressed, and training is more effective if it is concentrated in such a way that the system being trained is **isolated** from others, especially when training individual muscles or muscle groups. Also, for the body to increase its capacities, that is it's 'fitness', it is necessary to expose it to **progressive overload**, interspersed with adequate **recovery** periods. Once the demand is reduced or removed altogether, the training effects are seen to be **reversible** as 'fitness' is lost, thus the deconditioning effects of bed rest include a decrease in $\dot{V}_{O_2}$ max, blood volume, skeletal muscle mass and contractile strength; and increase in resting heart rate.

Training involves a fine balance between progressive overload and adequate recovery. Overtraining, where there is insufficient rest to allow recovery from training, leads to a decrease in athletic performance; just as would occur with insufficient overload and too much rest. This is why training schedules followed slavishly in the absence of a personal coach may be counterproductive. The main role of any coach is to know the athlete's response to the demands of training.

Adequate recovery is usually ensured by the **periodisation** of training over various periods of time or cycles. For example one method used in training endurance athletes in particular, is for three hard weeks to alternate with an easier one, for three hard months to alternate with an easier one, and for three hard years to alternate with an easier one. However, getting dedicated sports people to reduce their efforts, can be as difficult as motivating non-athletes to increase theirs.

All fitness training regimes can be designed to be **sport** or **game specific**, that is to take account of the special demands of a particular sport or game, for example running, swimming, cycling, rowing, canoeing, skiing etc. Game specific training incorporates the practice of skills whilst carrying out training of the fitness components, for example footballers would perform shuttle runs whilst trying to control a ball.

6.2 CONTINUOUS TRAINING REGIMES

Continuous running, swimming, or cycling etc. trains the aerobic capacity and increases endurance. Continuous 'steady state' effort, can be maintained for a considerable time at a certain intensity or percentage of the maximum aerobic power ($\dot{V}_{O_2}\,max$), in which the oxygen uptake matches the oxygen demand. During maximal work the cardiac output and oxygen uptake can be lower than at a lower work rate, also anaerobic processes are stressed which is not the prime objective. Therefore if the intensity is pitched at the right level, training at a sub-maximal effort is easier, and more effective in training aerobic capacity, than at maximal effort. One simple way to judge a manageable pace for aerobic training is to exercise just beyond that intensity at which conversation stops.

A more accurate measure is obtained by monitoring the heart rate/pulse, as it is a measure of the work being done by the heart. Karvonen recommended continuous effort at an intensity of about 66% of the heart rate reserve, that is the difference between the resting and the maximum heart rate.

(Maximum heart rate – Resting heart rate) $\times$ 2/3 = X
Resting heart rate + X = Aerobic endurance training level.

This represents a training intensity of about 50% of the $\dot{V}_{O_2}\,max$.

The maximum heart rate can be estimated theoretically by subtracting one's age from 220. However, it must be remembered that endurance training results in a slowing of the resting heart rate *(bradycardia)* and a lowering of the maximum heart rate. So that a twenty year old well conditioned male endurance athlete could find it difficult to raise their heart rate to 200 bpm, whatever their level of exertion.

As far as general endurance fitness is concerned, exercising at this level for thirty minutes three times a week, is recommended as being effective in promoting gains in aerobic endurance.

With the increasing availability of reliable lightweight heart rate monitors, much interest has been generated in using heart rates as indicators of training intensities.

The Conconi test involves monitoring the heart rate as an athlete slightly increases their speed until maximum effort. Up to a certain point the heart rate increases proportionally to the speed, but past that point the heart rate does not increase in proportion to the speed. This 'heart rate deflection point' is taken to represent the 'lactate or anaerobic threshold' or 'OBLA', in other words effort that is being made to increase speed that is not increasing the heart rate *(and therefore the delivery of oxygen to the tissues for aerobic respiration)* must be anaerobic. It is suggested that regularly training close to an athlete's current 'lactate threshold' is an effective way of improving endurance. However, the 'heart rate deflection point' can occur at much higher exercise intensities than the actual 'lactate threshold', often close to the maximum heart rate, at which point prolonged efforts could result in overtraining.

6.3 INTERMITTENT TRAINING REGIMES

These involve alternating periods of effort and recovery, and are based on the principle that the body can in this way be exposed to a greater total work load than it could be during a continuous period of exercise, when various limiting factors come into play. Almost limitless variations are possible with these regimes, as the number, duration and activity of the work and rest intervals can be altered to suit the aim of the training.

6.3.1 INTERVAL TRAINING.

Interval training can improve both aerobic and anaerobic powers, but its use as anaerobic conditioning is more effective after an extended period of aerobic conditioning.

In running, the original Gerschler-Reindell schedules were for a warm-up period that raised the heart rate to 120 bpm; then for a certain distance to be run in a given time to raise the heart rate to 170-180 bpm; followed by a recovery interval of less than 90 seconds in which the heart rate dropped back to 120 bpm. This in the body *(at least not at a fast enough rate to satisfy demand)* and must be obtained via the diet. Amino acids excess to the body's needs cannot be stored, and are converted into glucose which is used as an energy source, and urea which is excreted in the urine, and incidently in the sweat (especially during exercise when the kidneys have a reduced blood supply.

Amphetamine
A synthetic central nervous system stimulant related to adrenaline.

Anabolic Steroids
A group of ergogenic aids *(related to the male hormone testosterone)* that have an anabolic (protein building) effect, and to a greater or lesser extent an androgenic *(development of male characteristics)* effect on the body.

Anabolism
That aspect of metabolism involved in the building up *(synthesis)* of complex substances *(e.g. proteins)* from simpler substances *(e.g. amino acids)*. Requires energy in the form of ATP.

Anaerobic Exercise *(respiration)*
Exercise that demands more oxygen than can be supplied at the time, and which therefore results in the depletion of ATP-PC stores, and the incomplete oxidation of glucose with the accumulation of lactic acid.

Anaerobic Glycolysis
The initial stages in the oxidative breakdown of glucose in the cytoplasm of cells and muscle fibres, which does not directly involve oxygen, generates a relatively small amount of ATP from each glucose molecule very rapidly, and which in the shortage of oxygen leads to the accumulation of lactic acid.

Anaerobic Threshold
The 'point' at which, during exercise, the oxygen supply becomes insufficient to maintain aerobic respiration, so that anaerobic respiration becomes predominant, with the accumulation of lactic acid in the blood. Less used than previously, as overlap between aerobic and anaerobic respiration systems at all times of all types of exercise complicate the idea of a simple 'threshold'.

Analgesic
Pain killer e.g. aspirin.

Anoxia
Lack of oxygen in tissues.

Arterioles
Finer branches of arteries, with relatively narrow diameters, and involuntary muscle in their walls, the contraction of which leads to vaso-constriction, and the relaxation of which leads to vasodilation. When constricted *(narrowed)* there is a greater resistance to the flow of the blood and a raised blood pressure, and vice versa. Lead into the capillary beds.

Arterio-venous oxygen difference (a-$\bar{v}O_2$ diff)
the difference in oxygen content between the blood entering and that leaving the pulmonary capillaries.

Artery
Blood vessels carrying blood away from the heart, eventually dividing into arterioles.

Articulate
To connect by means of a joint.

ATP-PC System *(phosphagen system)*
An anaerobic energy system in which ATP is regenerated from the breakdown of phosphocreatine *(PC)*. Muscles performing at maximal effort obtain ATP from this system.

Atrophy
Reduction in size and/or mass of cells and tissues, especially relating to muscle fibres.

Autonomic
Self-controlling; functionally independent of voluntary control.

Autonomic Nervous System
That part of the nervous system which works involuntarily *(is not under voluntary control)*, controlling all the autonomic processes in the body, e.g. breathing rate, heart rate, peristalsis in the gut, contraction of the bladder, dilation and constriction of the pupil of the eye. Consists of two opposing *(antagonistic)* sub-systems, the sympathetic and parasympathetic nervous systems.

Basal Metabolic Rate
The rate of the metabolism, as measured by the energy output of an individual, whilst at rest in optimum conditions 12-18 hours after eating *(post-absorptive period)*.

Biopsy
The extraction of small pieces of tissues for chemical and/or histological studies, e.g. muscle biopsy to study fibre composition, using a hollow needle.

Blood Pressure
The pressure exerted by the blood on the wall of a blood vessel, a function of cardiac output and peripheral resistance *(the resistance to flow of the blood in the blood vessels, mainly the arterioles).*

Bradycardia
Resting heart rate slower than average.

Buffering capacity
The capacity to prevent changes in pH.

Buffers
Substances which can prevent rapid changes in pH *(acidity and alkalinity)* within the body, e.g. proteins in the plasma, and haemoglobin in the red cells of the blood.

Calorie
A unit of heat. A thousand so-called small calories equals one large Calorie *(kilocalorie or kcal),* which is the type used when speaking of human nutrition. 1 Calorie = 4186 joules (4.186 kJ).

Carbohydrates
Organic compound containing only carbon, hydrogen and oxygen in a characteristic ratio, e.g. starch, sucrose *(table sugar),* and glucose. They are a basic source of energy, circulating as glucose in the blood stream, and being stored as glycogen in virtually all body tissues, but mainly in the liver and muscles. Bread, potatoes, fruits, honey and refined sugars are all excellent sources of carbohydrates. Carbohydrates yield about four Calories per gram when oxidised.

Cardiac Output
The amount of blood in dm^3 (litres), pumped by the heart per minute, a function of heart rate and stroke volume. Generally the outputs of the right and left ventricles are the same.

Catabolism
That aspect of metabolism involved in the breakdown of complex substances into simpler substances. For example the oxidation of glucose into carbon dioxide and water *(with the release of energy)* in aerobic respiration.

Central nervous system
The brain and spinal cord.

Chemoreceptors
Receptors sensing changes in the chemical composition of body fluids e.g. blood glucose levels.

**Complete Protein
(protein of high biological value)**
Protein that contains all of the essential amino acids, e.g. eggs *(which contain them in the ratio closest to that of human requirements),* cheese, milk, meat, whole grains, and soya beans.

Concentric contraction
Contraction of a muscle reducing its length.

Connective Tissue
Tissues that provide support and cohesion for the body, e.g. white collagen fibres which form tendons, the basis of bone, and fibrous cartilage; yellow elastic fibres which form ligaments, and the basis of elastic cartilage; bone and cartilage. Others form sheets or mesenteries which hold organs in place.

Core Body Temperature
The central body temperature, as opposed to that of the limbs, the temperature of which is lower due to their greater surface area to volume ratio .

Coronary
Relating to the blood vessels that supply the cardiac muscle of the heart wall *(from their 'crown' like arrangement around the heart).*

Dehydration
Excessive loss of water, during exercise mainly as a result of sweating.

Diastole
Relaxation, as in relaxation of the ventricles *(ventricular diastole).*

Diffusion
The net movement of gases or dissolved substances, as a result of their kinetic energy, from regions of their higher concentration to regions of their lower concentration, down a concentration gradient, until equilibrium is reached.

Eccentric contraction
Contraction of a muscle whilst the length of the muscle increases, e.g. the contraction of the quadriceps in the front of the thigh whilst running downhill.

Stationary Air
The air remaining in the lungs during quiet tidal breathing.

Strength
The force that a muscle can exert in one maximal effort.

Stroke volume *(SV)*
The volume of blood ejected by each contraction *(systole)* of the ventricle, is calculated by dividing the cardiac output by the heart rate.

Superficial
On or near the surface, visible or palpable *(able to feel with hands).*

Sympathetic nervous system
The part of the autonomic *(involuntary)* nervous system responsible for preparing the body for action *(see adrenaline.)* Antagonistic to the parasympathetic nervous system.

Systemic circulation
The general circulatory system of the body, as opposed to that of the lungs (pulmonary circulation). Blood passes through the heart twice, as it flows from the systemic to the pulmonary and back to the systemic circulation.

Systole
Contraction, as in ventricular systole.

Tachycardia
Resting heart rate faster than average.

Temporal summation
An increase in responsiveness of a nerve or muscle fibre, resulting from the additive effect of frequently occurring stimuli.

Tendon
Tough, non elastic fibrous tissue attaching muscles to bones.

Testosterone
The male sex hormone secreted by the testes in the male, and by the adrenal cortex in both males and females. Responsible for the development of male characteristics.

Thorax
That part of the body containing the heart and the lungs, separated from the abdomen by the diaphragm.

Tidal volume
The volume of air moved during quiet breathing at rest.

Total lung capacity
Vital capacity + residual volume, difficult to measure.

Validity
A measure of whether a test actually tests what it claims to test, e.g. does the Conconi test give a measure of the anaerobic threshold?

Vasoconstriction
A decrease in the diameter of a blood vessel *(usually an arteriole)* by contraction of circular involuntary muscle fibres in the walls, resulting in a reduction of blood flow to the area supplied by the vessel.

Vasodilation
An increase in the diameter of a blood vessel *(usually an arteriole)* resulting in an increased blood flow to the area supplied by a vessel.

Vasomotor
Relating to the control of vasoconstriction and vasodilation.

Viscosity
'Thickness' of a fluid or 'ease of flow', e.g. plasma has a viscosity which allows it to be pumped rapidly around the body.

Vital Capacity
The total volume of air that can be expired following full inspiration, in other words the total volume of air that can be moved over the lungs in one 'breath'.

Vitamins
Complex organic substances required in the diet *(NB vitamin D also produced by the action of ultra-violet light on the skin)*, essential for normal body functions and maintenance of health. Vitamins contribute to the regulation of metabolic processes, including a role in energy transformations.

Work
Application of a force through a distance; it is measured in joules *(J, kJ, MJ).*

Work rate
Work performed per unit time = power.

INDEX